INSIDE THE
MOSCOW ART THEATRE

VLADIMIR NEMIROVITCH-DANTCHENKO AND CONSTANTIN
STANISLAVSKY

Founders of the Moscow Art Theatre, Celebrating the Twenty-fifth Anniversary
of the Theatre at Waren, Germany, in the Summer of 1923, Midway between the Two American Seasons of the Dramatic Company

INSIDE THE MOSCOW ART THEATRE

BY

OLIVER M. SAYLER 1887-

AUTHOR OF "THE RUSSIAN THEATRE," "RUSSIA WHITE OR RED,"
AND "OUR AMERICAN THEATRE," AND EDITOR OF
"MAX REINHARDT AND HIS THEATRE," ETC.

*WITH 8 ILLUSTRATIONS IN FULL COLORS
AND 106 IN BLACK AND WHITE*

BRENTANO'S

PUBLISHERS   NEW YORK

PN
2726
M6
53

Printed in the United States of America

TO

CONSTANTIN SERGEITCH
AND
VLADIMIR IVANITCH

IN ADMIRATION AND AFFECTION
FOR THE TWIN CREATORS OF THE
WORLD'S FOREMOST THEATRE

PREFACE

When I returned from Moscow seven years ago, laden with the data for "The Russian Theatre," I was confronted by the formidable temptation to limit myself to the fascinating story of the Moscow Art Theatre and to discard all of the rest of the material I had gathered. Fairness to the other notable stages of the two Russian capitals, however, in conjunction with the thought that comparison and contrast between the Art Theatre and its rivals might redound the more vividly to its reputation, combined to hold me to my original intention. "The Russian Theatre," therefore, was a comprehensive record of the activities of the entire contemporary dramatic movement in Russia. Fully one-third of this record, nevertheless, fell to the lot of the Art Theatre and its several studios.

If fidelity to the general subject justified the broad scope of "The Russian Theatre," the cycle of the years has brought me back to my original temptation with a logic that can not now be gainsaid. Much water has plunged under theatrical bridges in the last half decade—both in Russia and America. Moscow has seen the expansion of its Art Theatre by the birth and growth to maturity of the Musical Studio of Nemirovitch-Dantchenko, the lustiest of the new theatrical enterprises conceived in the day of social upheaval. America has played host for two seasons to Stanislavsky and the entire first line of the Art Theatre's Dramatic Company. Furthermore, the expansion of the Art Theatre in Moscow is being superimposed on its earlier foundation in this country by the fact that Morris Gest has cast America once more as host to the Art Theatre in the person of its Musical Studio.

With my sense of duty to the Russian theatre at large propitiated and with the Moscow Art Theatre now universally recognized, through redoubled achievement and tripled acquaintance, as the unique source of creative dramatic energy which I suspected seven years ago, I feel that the time has come for a full record of the intimate observations of its activities which I have had the privilege of collecting. I make no attempt here to retell those portions of the story of the Moscow Art Theatre which I recounted in "The Russian Theatre." Nor do I propose to repeat those chapters from its annals which Stanislavsky has told with such homely honesty and disarming naïveté in his autobiography, "My Life in Art." Instead, I resume the thread where "The Russian Theatre" left off, filling in occasional gaps in the earlier record. Rather than provide a dull and colorless chronicle of twenty-seven years of creative activity, I have preferred the attempt to sketch a vivid, human picture of the Moscow Art Theatre as it exists today—the largest, busiest, most influential organization devoted to dramatic art in the world.

To acknowledge my debt to all those who have attested their regard for the world's first theatre by assisting me in my task would be impossible. Those who have performed unique and indispensable services are: Dr. Sergei Berthensson, who gathered for me most of the historical and official data beyond my own reach; Olin Downes, Music Critic of *The New York Times,* who has verified my musical allusions; Morris Gest, whose passionate devotion to the Russian theatre prompted this volume; Simeon Gest, who has helped to clarify for me many of the apparent contradictions in the Russian spirit; Charles J. Herold, of Brentano's, who has stood by as counsellor while this work grew from a project for a modest monograph to a full-length book; and my wife, Lucie R. Sayler, for assistance with the proofs.

OLIVER M. SAYLER.

New York City,
  December, 1925.

CONTENTS

LIST OF ILLUSTRATIONS

[xiii]

List of Illustrations

List of Illustrations

[xv]

List of Illustrations

INSIDE THE MOSCOW ART THEATRE

CHAPTER I

INSIDE THE ART THEATRE TODAY

QUIETLY, unobtrusively, without either the fanfare of open diplomacy or the suspicion of its secret sister, a generous sample of the soul of America has eluded the customs barriers and the pass frontiers between the port of New York and the capital of Russia. I am not sure that the members of the Moscow Art Theatre realize even yet that this potent but imponderable commodity traveled as stowaway in their luggage on their return home. The stock on hand of American soul is always so large that we haven't missed the absence of this particular portion of it. But, if I read American character aright, the story of how it got to Moscow and what it is doing there, as well as the implications of further export traffic in soul, both Russian and American, will satisfy a certain naïve trait in us.

Like children, we pick up ideas from abroad quickly and improve on them or adapt them to our needs. Like children, we give our visitors from abroad about twenty-four hours grace and then ask them what they think of us. Like children, we are especially happy when we hear that other countries have adopted something or somebody or some idea

[1]

that belongs to us. It is a childlike trait, too, when we are secretly a bit surprised and at the same time take it quite as a matter of fact that they have done so. It seems perfectly natural to us that Europe and the universe have accepted our motion pictures, our jazz, our phonographs, our sewing-machines, Ford cars, Eugene O'Neill. And yet it gives us a furtive thrill whenever Douglas Fairbanks smiles at us from a theatrical poster in Venice, whenever a grind-organ awakens us from sleep in a Tyrolean hotel with "Yes, We Have No Bananas," whenever a flivver chugs up to the station in Omsk to take us through Siberian mud into town. Our two years, therefore, as hosts to the Moscow Art Theatre, the year that has elapsed since the Russians left us, and their return, singing and acting, in the form of the Art Theatre's Musical Studio, present an excellent opportunity to view these international processes in action.

The detailed record of the American adventure, gathered together for the first time between book covers, I shall reserve for the following chapter. Here I propose to afford a glimpse inside the Art Theatre today, to show its intricate organization at work and to trace the effects of the long sojourn with us. For perspective for this survey, it is necessary only to recall the deliberate, ponderous methods of this theatre and its artists before they had caught the contagions of America, methods which I recounted in "The Russian Theatre," with irritation tempered by respect. Red tape, delay, needless formality. It required four months, for instance, back in 1918, to obtain the release of certain prints for a trusted photographer to copy! Only the perfection of their work and the graciousness of their spirit made the game of gathering their story worth the fretful candle.

In marked contrast today, there is order, efficiency, speed, adaptability, readiness to meet unusual situations. And all this without sacrificing in the least the tradition of thoroughness and care on which the theatre was founded. Perhaps you will say that this transformation should be charged to the Revolution rather than to the company's sojourn in America. The Revolution, it is true, turned many necessities into luxuries. It put a prohibitive tax on the prerogatives of inefficiency. Moreover, the Revolution made it possible for Morris Gest to induce the company ever to leave home. Until these pampered and privileged Russians visited us, however, they resented change. Today, they are proud of their aptness in applying the lessons of change America taught them. As one of them characteristically remarked on leaving us: "Accustomed as we always have been to a terrific amount of work, after our stay in America and having witnessed how much people in this country work, we came to the conclusion that one may work nearly twenty-four hours a day."

I don't say that the entire company is America-broke. Ivan Moskvin, for instance, carried his hotel key in his pocket for the entire two years for fear he wouldn't know how to ask for it. Then there is the story which Olga Knipper-Tchehova tells on herself of how she descended into the subway, found no nickels in her purse and plugged dimes into the turnstile until Moskvin rescued her, bruised and winded from pushing on the unyielding gate. Interviews, too, and all the weird expedients of American pub-

[3]

licity, which are commonplace in the lives of our own players, still seem inexplicable to these Russians, although irritation over them has given way to toleration, mild amusement and recognition of their apparent efficacy.

On the whole, however, these visitors of ours learned our ways surprisingly well. They took to heart especially our admonitions: "Do it now," "Everything is possible," "I'll try anything once," "Time is money." Step inside any one of the three buildings devoted to the Art Theatre's activities today and you will find a hive of efficient energy. Four companies operate on these three stages: 1, the Dramatic Company we know; 2, the Musical Studio, to which is being entrusted the further fate and fame of the Sea-Gull on our shores; 3, the Moscow Art Theatre, Second, the old First Studio grown up; and 4, the Dramatic Studio and School. The 1st and 2nd may be seen on the parent stage in the old Kamergersky Pereulok, which the Soviet has renamed the Street of the Moscow Art Theatre; the 1st and 3rd in the huge Novy or New Theatre (formerly the Nezlobina) flanking the Great State Theatre in the Theatre Square; and the 2nd and 4th in a spacious old building, around the corner from the Art Theatre in the Tverskaya, which was used during the war as a soldiers' club by the American Y. M. C. A.

In a week's time, therefore, upwards of sixteen different plays and operettas are offered to the public on these three stages. An eight-day cross section out of this busy life, copied from the bulletin board outside the front entrance to the theatre during my visit last December, reveals the following range of choice:

[4]

In the Moscow Art Theatre:

Tues., Dec. 9, 1924, "Carmencita and the Soldier" (Bizet-Mérimée), by the Musical Studio.

Wed., Dec. 10, "Tsar Fyodor Ivanovitch" (Tolstoy), by the Dramatic Company.

Thurs., Dec. 11, "The Daughter of Madame Angot" (Lecocq), by the Musical Studio.

Fri., Dec. 12, "Lysistrata" (Aristophanes), by the Musical Studio.

Sat., Dec. 13, "The Death of Pazuhin" (Saltuikoff-Shchedrin), by the Dramatic Company.

Sun., Dec. 14, matinee, "The Blue Bird" (Maeterlinck), by the Dramatic Company; evening, "La Périchole" (Offenbach), by the Musical Studio.

Mon., Dec. 15 (All Theatres "dark"; weekly holiday by Government decree).

Tues., Dec. 16, "The Lower Depths" (Gorky), by the Dramatic Company.

In the Moscow Art Theatre, Second:

Tues., Dec. 9, "The Lower Depths" (Gorky), by the Dramatic Company of the Moscow Art Theatre.

Wed., Dec. 10, "Hamlet" (Shakespeare), by the Company of the Moscow Art Theatre, Second.

Thurs., Dec. 11, "The Spendthrift" (Lieskoff), by the Company of the Moscow Art Theatre, Second.

Fri., Dec. 12, "Love—The Golden Book" (Tolstoy), by the Company of the Moscow Art Theatre, Second.

Sat., Dec. 13, "Hamlet" (Shakespeare), by the Company of the Moscow Art Theatre, Second.

Sun., Dec. 14, "King Lear" (Shakespeare), by the Company of the Moscow Art Theatre, Second.

[5]

Mon., Dec. 15 ("Dark").

Tues., Dec. 16, "Twelfth Night" (Shakespeare), by the Company of the Moscow Art Theatre, Second.

In the Dramatic Studio of the Moscow Art Theatre:

Tues., Dec. 9, "The Battle of Life" (Dickens), by the School.

Wed., Dec. 10, "The Fairy Lady" (Calderon), by the Dramatic Studio.

Thurs., Dec. 11, "The Battle of Life," by the School.

Fri., Dec. 12, "Youth" (Andreieff), by the Dramatic Studio.

Sat., Dec. 13, "The Fairy Lady," by the Dramatic Studio.

Sun., Dec. 14, "The Battle of Life," by the School.

Mon., Dec. 15 ("Dark").

Tues., Dec. 16, "The Daughter of Madame Angot" (Lecocq), by the Musical Studio.

All these productions, of course, are kept at a keen edge and new ones are in process of preparation under the Art Theatre's justly-famed régime of constant and thorough rehearsal. I copied several typical daily rehearsal schedules from the call board, and I know of nothing which will visualize, so clearly as these lists do, the air of nervous tension which pervades every nook of this theatre even during the hours when there is no public present to provide a stimulus to the players.

Here, for example, is a rehearsal day for the Dramatic Company:

11 A. M. In the Studio "The Blue Bird," in charge of V. S. Alexeieff, a Call for all the Black People, the Dishes, Clocks, Spirits, Horrors and Stars.

[6]

11 A. M.   In the Upper Foyer "The Mistress of the Inn," in charge of Nina Litovtseva, Scenes from the First and Second Act.

11 A. M.   On the New Stage "Pugatchovshchina," in charge of Leonid M. Leonidoff, Episodes from the Sixth Scene.

12 Noon.   In Stanislavsky's Dressing Room "Pugatchovshchina," in charge of Vassily Luzhsky, the First Scene.

12 Noon.   In the New Students' Dressing Room "The Sorrows of the Spirit," in charge of N. M. Gortchakoff, Scenes involving Sofia (A. O. Stepanova) and Tchatsky (Y. A. Zovadsky).

12 Noon.   In the Studio "The Blue Bird," in charge of V. S. Alexeieff, Scene of the Christmas Tree with Tyltyl and Mytyl.

1 P. M.   At Stanislavsky's Home "The Blue Bird," the Third Scene, "In the Land of Memory," a call for everyone appearing in this scene.

1 P. M.   In the Lower Foyer "The Blue Bird," in charge of B. I. Vershiloff, the Fourth Scene, "Night," a call for everyone appearing in this scene.

2 P. M.   In the Upper Foyer "The Stone Guest," in charge of Nina Litovtseva, First and Third Scenes, a call for the entire cast.

2:30 P. M.   In the Lower Foyer "The Blue Bird," the Fifth Scene, "The Kingdom of the Future," a call for everyone appearing in this scene.

It might be suspected from this schedule that a performance of Maeterlinck's fairy play was somewhere in the offing. And it was—the next afternoon, Sunday, Stanislavsky's almost weekly contribution to the joy of the children of Moscow. No one but the Art Theatre, though, would deem it necessary to rehearse a play that had been performed from thirty to fifty times a season for the last fifteen years!

The best proof that the new Musical Studio is a true child of the Sea-Gull is a typical rehearsal schedule from its own call board:

11 A. M.   In the Upper Foyer Rachmaninoff's "Aleko," in charge of K. I. Kotlubai and E. F. Tserteleva, a Musical Rehearsal with Soloists.

11 A. M.   In the Ladies' Foyer "Lysistrata," in charge of M. M. Popoff, Choral Rehearsal of the New Group.

12 Noon.   In the Ladies' Foyer "The Daughter of Madame Angot," in charge of A. V. Mitropolsk, Musical Practice for Ivan Velikanoff in the rôle of Ange Pitou.

12 Noon.   In the Music Room "La Périchole," in charge of Y. A. Skatkina, Musical Practice for Regina Preval in the rôle of the French Court Lady.

12 Noon.   In the Lower Foyer "Boris Godunoff," in charge of Constantin Shvedoff, Choral Rehearsal, all Tenors called.

12:45 P. M.   In the Lower Foyer The Same, all Altos called.

1:15 P. M.   In the Lower Foyer The Same, all Basses called.

12:45 P. M.   In the Artists' Dressing Room "The Daughter of Madame Angot," in charge of Vladimir Lossky, Scenes involving Pomponnet (A. V. Obukhoff).

1 P. M.   In the New Students' Dressing Room "The Daughter of Madame Angot," in charge of V. V. Protasievitch, Scenes involving Buteux (V. G. Tchukoff).

1 P. M.   In the Music Room "La Périchole," in charge of Y. A. Skatkina, Musical Practice for Ivan Velikanoff in the rôle of Piquillo.

[8]

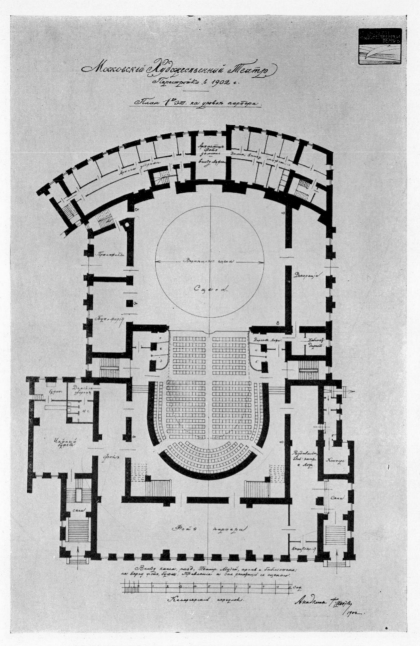

GROUND PLAN OF THE MOSCOW ART THEATRE

Architect's Drawing, dated 1902, for the Reconstruction of the Second and Present Home, Showing the Promenade Foyer, the Restaurant (at the left), the Orchestra Seating Plan, the Stage with the Revolving Turntable and the Row of Dressing Rooms for the Women

A CLASS OF THE MUSICAL STUDIO
Practicing Rhythmic Exercises under the Direction of Leonid Baratoff

A CORNER OF THE MUSEUM OF THE MOSCOW ART THEATRE
Devoted to the Musical Studio's Production of "Carmencita and the Soldier"

1:15 P. M. On the Large Stage "La Périchole," in charge of L. K. Redega, Dances of the Peruvian Sisters.

2 P. M. In the New Artists' Dressing Room "The Daughter of Madame Angot," in charge of V. V. Protasievitch, Scenes in the Second Act involving Hersilie (M. A. Grube).

2 P. M. On the Large Stage "La Périchole," in charge of Leonid Baratoff, Stage Business for the Peruvian Sisters.

2:30 P. M. In the New Artists' Dressing Room "The Daughter of Madame Angot," in charge of V. V. Protasievitch, Scenes involving Louchard (K. I. Obolensky).

2:45 P. M. In the Artists' Dressing Room "The Daughter of Madame Angot," in charge of Vladimir Lossky, Scenes involving Louchard (Dmitry Kamernitsky).

7 P. M. In the Hall K. O. "Carmencita and the Soldier," in charge of Vladimir Nemirovitch-Dantchenko, Scenes involving Lucas (Pyotr Saratovsky).

8 P. M. In the Hall K. O. "Carmencita and the Soldier," in charge of Vladimir Nemirovitch-Dantchenko, Scenes involving Lucas (Pyotr Saratovsky) and José (Ivan Velikanoff).

In this case, the performance of the evening was "La Périchole," and the large number of rehearsals for "The Daughter of Madame Angot" was due to training new singers for rotation of rôles.

To chart these elaborate rehearsal schedules, not to mention the performances themselves, and to do so in a single crowded building without confusion and without one company treading on the toes of the other, is the work of a train-dispatcher. No wonder Stanislavsky and Nemirovitch-Dantchenko are dissatisfied with the Art Theatre's theatre.

[9]

No wonder they consider it an antiquated structure, even in the face of the affection they feel for the scenes of their life-long labors. No wonder they long for the new home of which they were cheated by war and revolution.

And yet, despite the fact that the theatre today is used beyond its comfortable capacity, despite the fact that only its stage was built new in 1902 and the rest of the edifice was the result of adroit remodeling of an existing building, its arrangement may serve in many respects as a prototype for theatres yet to be erected. When you enter under the spreading wings of the Sea-Gull, you are struck at every turn by the fitness of everything for the appointed task. Commodious cloak-rooms for the severe Russian winter. A foyer as spacious as an esplanade, large enough to accommodate almost the entire audience in its between-acts Russian marathon. A restaurant opening off it, as quiet and dignified as a reception room at home. An auditorium—parterre, with four boxes that aren't really boxes; balcony, and gallery—with excellent sight lines from each of the 1,200 seats. And those seats simple and comfortable, with no sleep-inducing upholstery. Simplicity, Severity and the Sea-Gull, in fact, are the three S's of the Art Theatre's interior decoration. So much you see as a casual visitor.

Back of the curtain, another world opens. Here you are really inside the Art Theatre. A stage larger than the auditorium! A turn-table, operated by electricity, which is cut in three transverse sections or platforms that may be raised or lowered at will. An excellent cyclorama which the directors would willingly exchange, however, for a plaster horizon. A scene dock, shut off by a fire wall, that will take care of half a dozen productions. And finally that mysterious double row of rooms along a curving corridor at the extreme rear of the plan—perhaps the distinguishing feature of this unusual structure. No American theatre builder and probably few in the world would suspect that these were the dressing rooms. Nor does the plan tell the entire story. The rooms of the men are on a level slightly below that of the stage. Immediately overhead, an equal distance above the stage, the same space is devoted to the women of the company. The less important players share their rooms. So do old cronies. But when a player like Stanislavsky or Olga Knipper-Tchehova comes to America, his room is locked for the two years!

Even now, our survey is not complete. Beneath the foyer, on the street level, is the box-office. Here still, as in the old days of Russian peace and plenty, you stand in line at the height of the season for a number, returning later in the day to see whether your ticket is the lucky one out of four or five drawn in a lottery and entitling you to buy seats. To the left of the box-office are the financial and business offices, luxuriously equipped with the furniture of certain members of the company who have had to give up their old quarters as a result of Moscow's housing congestion.

To the right of the box-office is the new Museum, crammed with trophies of the twenty-seven years of the theatre's history as well as of its predecessors—the Alexeieff (Stanislavsky) Circle, the Society of Art and Literature, and the Philharmonic Society. Manifestly, it is possible to display at a given time only a small proportion of the accumulation of over three decades, in the form of programs, press

[11]

clippings, stage and costume designs, models, posters, photographs, prompt-books, pamphlets and other publications, etc., etc. And so exhibitions, open to the public, are arranged here from the library vaults up under the roof.

Nor does the plan show the executive offices or the smoking and retiring rooms that occupy the floors above the foyer. An entire new wing, too, has recently been added to the left front of the building, which gives additional space for rehearsals.

All this would seem to preclude the need for a new Moscow Art Theatre. But when we stop to consider that the birth of the Musical Studio has practically doubled the strain on the capacities of plant and structure in the last five years, the attitude of the directors becomes plausible. The profits of the American adventure of the Dramatic Company went toward keeping at pre-war standards the old structure at a time when every other playhouse in Moscow was—and still is—cold, dirty, out of repair and down at the heels. Whether the prospective profits of the Musical Studio in this country will be devoted toward a new home for itself, like those of the Moscow Art Theatre, Second, and the Dramatic Studio and School, or possibly serve as a nest-egg for a new common home large enough for both companies, only time and the return of economic stability in Russia can tell.

Meanwhile, it is a case of "carry on!" And to do so efficiently, a new and autocratic form of organization has been devised, regretfully replacing the old coöperative system that had endured so long. Under the new regime, all four companies and all three stages are responsible solely to Nemirovitch-Dantchenko, instead of to the Council of char-

y The Moscow Art
Music by Reinhold

ter members. Stanislavsky alone is autonomous as adviser to the Dramatic Studio and School. The circumstances, details and significance of this revolutionary change will be considered in Chapter III. It is enough here to note that Stanislavsky and the Council, practically all of whom were in America at the time the change was proposed, adopted it unanimously after observing the results of centralized power in our American business and theatre management.

In minor and personal ways, too, the daily life of the members of the company is linked up with America. By reduced salaries the Art Theatre is trying courageously to wipe out a huge deficit resulting from its determination to continue making new productions and to keep the old ones and the theatre itself in ship-shape, and it is America, indirectly, which makes this course feasible. One of the leading actresses, unselfishly coöperating in this effort to balance accounts, accepts a salary inferior to that which she received when the theatre was founded and she was an unknown amateur. Even the two founders of the theatre draw a smaller number of rubles in a month's time than an average American actor demands in dollars per week. Go into Moscow's apparel shops and see how far such salaries will take you—a pair of shoes, forty rubles or twenty dollars; a man's ordinary suit of clothes, two hundred rubles or one hundred dollars; and everything else in proportion. What saves the artists and their appearance, of course, is the wardrobe each of them was able to lay by against a dubious future while they were here.

Gone are the days when you could talk English in the corridors for secrecy's sake. French and German have been most emphatically superseded by English as the second language within these walls. Players who were timid with their English while with us, have gained strange assurance back home. Many of them, for practice, write letters to their English instructors in America and receive them back corrected. And the moment the prospect dawned of a trip to America for the Musical Studio, the eager young men and women making up this company bought out the supply of English grammars in the bookshops and plied their elders, who had been to our distant land, for lessons, turning the little restaurant, opening off the foyer, into a schoolroom. I never had a meal there when one or more of them did not approach my table and naïvely attempt a visit in English for practice' sake.

The most emphatic evidence that the Moscow Art Theatre has undergone a sea-change, however, may be found in the tours to the provinces which the company has made since its return home. In the old days, before the American experience, an excursion from Moscow was looked upon as a pilgrimage, an affair of state, to be approached with months of preparation and to be carried out with the aid of special trains and private cars. In that way the Art Theatre made its annual descent on Petersburg at the end of each season, until the war congested the Russian railways and kept the company at home. In that way the pilgrimage to the Crimea was made in 1900 to show Tchehoff his own plays in his southern exile. In that way the grand tour of Germany, Poland and Austria was carried out in 1906.

It was this same conception of an ordinary railroad trip as an expedition into the desert which threatened to balk Morris

Gest's desire to exhibit his Russian proteges to Chicago, Boston and other American cities. Three days were stipulated by the Council of the theatre as the necessary interval between engagements—one for traveling and two for getting accustomed to the new stage. Gest disregarded their ultimatum, routed them like an American traveling company, and trusted to American stage hands to open Russian eyes and temper Russian prerogatives without injuring Russian artistic standards. Within three hours after the train had reached Chicago, the barbaric walls of the Kremlin Castle were in place on the stage of the Great Northern Theatre, ready for the first rehearsal of "Tsar Fyodor Ivanovitch." After that there was no further argument. The Russian knows how to quit fighting gracefully.

Witness, then, the way the American lessons in traveling and transportation have been applied since the return to Moscow: Partly to eke out the treasury and partly to satisfy the aroused taste for "something doing," frequent trips have been made to nearby Russian cities and towns, not only by the Dramatic Company but also by the Musical Studio, to whom their elders taught the tricks learned in America. In this way, for the first time, such Russian communities as Tula, Nizhni-Novgorod, Tver, Ivanovo-Voznesensk and Oryehovo-Zuyevo, have been enabled to see the fountain-head of the modern Russian stage at work. Many of these trips have been made under conditions which would start a rebellion among the most seasoned wayfarers on the American one-night stands. But Russians never learn lessons halfway, and the players have entered on each of these outings just as if it were a great lark. A quite Ameri-

[15]

can pamphlet-prospectus of these tours has been issued, containing generous references to the American adventure and its sponsor, Morris Gest.

Take for example the engagements in Oryehovo-Zuyevo, a trip that has been made oftener than anywhere else, in view of the fact that this town, about sixty or seventy-five versts from Moscow, is the site of a great factory founded by the late Savva Morozoff, Mæcenas of the Moscow Art Theatre in its early days of struggle. Morozoff commissioned the same architect who designed the Art Theatre to build a playhouse for his workmen. And here, among other productions, the Musical Studio has given "The Daughter of Madame Angot" and "La Périchole," and the Dramatic Company has appeared in "The Death of Pazuhin," using the drape scenery evolved for the American production of the comedy.

Now, there are only two trains a day to Oryehovo-Zuyevo. To leave in the morning would waste an entire day. Therefore the company sets out from Moscow at 5:30 in the afternoon, arriving about eight. The performance begins at 10:30 P. M. and the final curtain falls after 2 A. M. Likewise, there are only two trains back, and, to avoid killing another day and arriving late for the evening performance in Moscow, the return trip is made between the hours of 7:30 and 10 A. M. If anyone had suggested that such a timetable was possible five years ago, his sanity would have been called in question.

And the most surprising thing about it all is that the prime mover, not only in these trips, but also in the increased general efficiency of the Moscow Art Theatre today, is Nemirovitch-Dantchenko, who has caught the contagion

THE INTERIOR OF THE MOSCOW ART THEATRE IN FACT AND IN
FANCY

Above, the Art Theatre Today. Below, the Architect's Drawing for the Reconstruction in 1902. A Border of Lights in Front of the Proscenium is Incorporated
in the Decorative Design.

UNCONVENTIONAL ASPECTS OF THE MOSCOW ART THEATRE

The Art Theatre from the Courtyard in the Rear, Showing the Extension below the Stage Loft Devoted to Dressing Rooms, and the Carpenter Shop to the Right

The Entrance to the Offices of the Art Theatre down an Alleyway from the Street, Showing the Wave Motive from the Sea-Gull Insignia Used in the Canopy

from his fellow-workers without ever yet having set foot on our soil. When he comes with his Musical Studio, the Moscow Art Theatre is likely to receive a further infusion of American soul, just as our imagination will again be stirred by that stimulus which is the peculiar possession of the Russians.

CHAPTER II

America, a Second Home

ONE of the most striking phenomena of our contemporary stage is the way the Russian Theatre has found a second home in America. Whether you are one of the majority who consider the title deed to this home honorably acquired, or whether you find flaws in it, there is no denying the fact. The deed is a matter of record. The bare statistics, regardless of the less tangible factors of mutual influence, prove the fact and prove it unique. Limiting ourselves to the company with which we are presently concerned, the Moscow Art Theatre gave a total of 380 performances of thirteen productions in twelve American cities in the course of two seasons. If that is not an American record for a visiting company playing wholly in a foreign tongue, it becomes so when multiplied by the attendance figures. The unusual nature of this reception is even more apparent when we remember that this same company, en route to us, tarried less than a month each in Berlin and Paris and that London hasn't risked the rôle of host at all. The recurrence of the phenomenon, therefore, with the Moscow Art Theatre Musical Studio coming to prove and retain the claim staked out by Balieff's Chauve-Souris and the Art Theatre's Dramatic Company, justifies an attempt to explain and understand it.

If anyone thinks that this phenomenon can be waved aside as a fad, a lucky throw of the dice or merely the result of shrewd showmanship, he is mistaken. Undoubtedly, these external factors contributed to the outcome, especially the third. America has a penchant for trailing the season's novelty with hue and cry. The adventure of the Art Theatre was timed fortunately not only to give needed respite from trying conditions at home but also to take advantage of a taste for all things Russian created here by the vogue of Balieff's Chauve-Souris. And finally, it is difficult to over-estimate the services of Morris Gest as synthetic principle in fusing foreign player and native spectator, Russian guest and American host, into a state of mutual respect and appreciation.

Nevertheless, there are other reasons, not so obvious— reasons that give potent aid to these external factors and remove the phenomenon from the realm of the accidental and the artificial, the factitious and the evanescent. On these fundamental reasons, the title deed of the Russian Theatre's second home must ultimately rest. Let us see what they are. First of all, the Russian Theatre has a vitality, an intensity, unparalleled in our time. Why it is thus favored and what that passionate intensity implies, I tried to make clear in "The Spirit of the Russian Theatre," the final chapter of my previous book on the subject. Of this characteristic there is nothing new to say except that, in the first place, it has found ever-broadening channels of expression at home and, in the second, ever-expanding opportunities for demonstration abroad, particularly in our own country.

The second fundamental factor, therefore, is the vitality and intensity of American life. Thus far, with few exceptions, our artists have lacked either the courage, the maturity or the technique to give literary, musical or dramatic expression to these traits that lie at the heart of our seething industrial and urban existence and stoke its fires. Lacking our own esthetic sublimation of these instincts, we respond the more readily to that which is brought us from abroad. "Something reached out to us across the footlights," said Stanislavsky after that first performance at Jolson's Fifty-Ninth Street Theatre, "and that something touched and thrilled us just as if a hand had been placed in our own." And again, at the end of the two seasons here, he wrote in his open letter of farewell to the American press: "No people feels so deeply as the American people, and in that respect the American soul and the Russian soul are very near to one another."

Closely related to this vital and passionate intensity of feeling—creative on the part of the Russians, receptive on our part—is the essential humanity of Russian dramatic art. Like all the greatest art, it has form without becoming stereotyped, it is intelligent without becoming intellectualized. Not only is it human, but it is colorful, releasing our pent-up love of color and bidding us be unashamed of it.

Still other factors have played their rôles. New York primarily and half a dozen other American cities possess a large public to whom Russian is a mother tongue and to whom the Moscow Art Theatre is the esthetic law and the prophets. Here, then, was the back-log of the fireplace, insuring an advance sale of such enormous proportions as to rivet the attention not only of the alert and the casual playgoer but also of the merely curious. Then, too, we must remember that our intelligent classes, to whom the Russian visitors naturally appeal most strongly, are less hard-pressed economically than in any country in the world. And finally, the Moscow Art Theatre came in full force, not with a handful of genuine artists and a ruck of hangers-on—a fact which appealed to the American sense of fair play, of good measure, "heaped up and running over."

Public judgment has both overrated and underrated Morris Gest's rôle in coördinating all these factors and putting them to work. When we bear in mind the natural elements conducive to success which we have just enumerated, it is manifestly unfair to everyone concerned to infer, as more than one jealous actor and manager has done, that he molded a gold brick and palmed it off with superb skill on an unsuspecting populace. It is just as unfair to ignore or belittle his influence. It is impossible to conceive of the Moscow Art Theatre in America without a soil congenial to it; it is just as impossible to conceive of it growing to bud and to flower without a master gardener to tend it. As I put it in "Our American Theatre": "In a very real sense, Gest 'produced' the Moscow Art Theatre. Stanislavsky and Nemirovitch-Dantchenko produced the plays. . . . But Gest produced the theatre. He served as the connecting link, interpreter, between the Russians and their American audience, instinctively understanding both better than either did the other. . . ."

How he did it would fill a text-book on publicity, propaganda and public relations: by enlisting the interest of patrons and sponsors in the walks of society, art, letters and the stage itself; by coöperation with the magazines and newspapers in providing a mass of information so that he

[21]

who ran might read and be unable to plead ignorance; by the publication of books and pamphlets and translations of the entire repertory; by printing a program that visualized the action step by step for those who knew no Russian; by capitalizing the visitors' idiosyncrasies, such as the ban on applause and on the interruptions of latecomers. Broadway will never cease to chortle over the way a veteran critic, a leading patron, and the owner of the theatre were kept warming themselves with their own wrath in the January lobby because they arrived two minutes after the curtain rose on the opening night. In short, Gest got the Moscow Art Theatre talked about, and he kept it talked about until it became "the thing to see." And if a few disgruntled souls resent that pressure, thousands are silently grateful for it.

Why Gest did it is not so easy to analyze. There is, of course, the legend perpetuated by Gilbert W. Gabriel, which tells of the meeting of Gest and Stanislavsky:

" 'Do you know why I brought the Moscow Art Theatre to America?' they say Gest demanded of the venerable player, throwing wide his arms and tossing his big, suffused eyes on high. 'Do you think it was for money, or fame, or anything like that? No, it was because my dear old father and mother, back there in Russia, would see in the newspaper that their son, their Morris in far-away America, had the power to bring the most famous actors in the world on a journey of five thousand miles. . . .

"The suave, slightly impatient Stanislavsky is said to have interrupted him: 'My dear Mr. Gest, I am exceedingly sorry, but I fear that we can not do business on the basis of your father and mother.' "

[22]

No, it was not for money. No gambler ever took so long a chance. As for fame, who knows? But whether it was wholly for the Russian father and mother, certainly the Russian heritage of Morris Gest stands potent in the background. Deep within his soul, which is more American than that of many scions of *Mayflower* blood, is a boundless passion for the art of his native land. And when he loves something, he frets and burns until he has persuaded others to love it, too.

In its revised form, "The Russian Theatre" brought the record of this company up to October, 1922, the eve of its arrival in New York. I shall not attempt here to repeat or even to summarize that record. To complete it briefly, to bring it up to date, however, may help us to follow more clearly its present and future paths.

Promptly at 8 o'clock on the evening of January 8, 1923, the curtain of Jolson's Fifty-Ninth Street Theatre, New York, rose on the play with which the Moscow Art Theatre has invariably begun an engagement since it has been a theatre, Count Alexei Tolstoy's barbaric pageant of an elder if not of a wholly departed Russia, "Tsar Fyodor Ivanovitch." Presented for a week, it gave way in turn to Gorky's "The Lower Depths" and to Tchehoff's "The Cherry Orchard" and "The Three Sisters." The house had been sold out in advance for the first eight weeks, resulting in the largest box-office receipts hitherto known for a dramatic company, playing either in a foreign language or in English. The first New York engagement lasted twelve weeks on a repertory basis, disclosing a fifth production consisting of

[23]

three scenes from Dostoievsky's "The Brothers Karamazoff" and Turgenieff's "The Lady from the Provinces."

Meanwhile, Chicago, Philadelphia and Boston had been petitioning Gest to give them an opportunity to play host to the visitors. Reluctantly at first, as I have told in the preceding chapter, the company set out for the west on Sunday, April 1. Three weeks at the Great Northern Theatre in Chicago were followed by two at the Lyric in Philadelphia and two at the Majestic in Boston. Everywhere the opening night and the farewell were ovations. In Boston, the city accorded official greeting, with the Russian ceremony of bread and salt. And if every seat was not filled at every performance, the result of the tour was still a triumph. A final fortnight in New York brought the first season to a brilliant close, June 2, 1923.

Knowing that life in Moscow was still onerous, Gest induced his distinguished proteges to return the following autumn, after a vacation in Central and Western Europe, although he and they knew that his attention and energies would have to be shared with Duse, Reinhardt and "The Miracle," and other commitments. Bringing a repertory of eight new plays and three old ones, the Art Theatre opened its second season, again at Jolson's in New York, on November 19, 1923, with a full evening's version of "The Brothers Karamazoff." Critical acclaim was the reward once more for this and the other new productions. And although the faddists trailed off after other gods, having done their Russian "bit," attendance throughout the season would have meant substantial profits for any ordinary company. As it was, the losses ate only sparingly into the balance of the first

THREE ASPECTS OF DEMENTIA

Vassily Katchaloff as Ivan Karamazoff, the Peak of the Company's Acting Achievements in America, in Dostoievsky's "The Brothers Karamazoff"

IVAN KARAMAZOFF (VASSILY KATCHALOFF) WRINGS THE CONFESSION OF MURDER FROM SMERDYAKOFF (LYOFF BULGAKOFF)

KATERINA IVANOVNA (LYDIA KORENIEVA) FEARS AND DISTRUSTS THE VOLUPTUOUS GRUSHENKA (ALLA TARASOVA)

SUSPICIONS, INSINUATING AND VIOLENT, IN DOSTOIEVSKY'S "THE BROTHERS KARAMAZOFF"

season. By returning without the glamor of novelty, the Moscow Art Theatre proved that it had won a secure place in American regard and American affections. Twelve weeks and three engagements in New York, making a grand total of twenty-six for the two seasons, were supplemented by three more weeks in Chicago, one more each in Philadelphia and Boston, and a break into fresh territory with a week each in Washington, Pittsburgh, Cleveland, Detroit, Brooklyn and Newark and three days each in New Haven and Hartford.

An idea of the relative popularity of the plays in the American repertory of the Art Theatre may be gained from the following summary of performances:

"Tsar Fyodor Ivanovitch," first season, 57; second season, 26; total, 83

"The Lower Depths," first season, 52; second season, 23; total, 75

"The Cherry Orchard," first season, 32; second season, 33; total, 65

"The Brothers Karamazoff" (full-length version), second season, 27

"Uncle Vanya," second season, 27

"The Three Sisters," first season, 25

"Ivanoff," second season, 21

"The Death of Pazuhin," second season, 15

"An Enemy of the People," second season, 12

"The Brothers Karamazoff" (short version), and "The Lady from the Provinces," first season, 10

"The Mistress of the Inn," second season, 9

"Enough Stupidity in Every Wise Man," second season, 5

[25]

"In the Claws of Life," second season, 5
Mixed Farewell Bill, second season, 1

But the annals of the Moscow Art Theatre in America are not all comprised in statistics. The members of the company had their play days as well as their work days. There is food for thought in the fact that they stole away at every opportunity to the negro cabarets in Harlem and to our musical comedies, and there is not a little irony in the fact that they chafed at accepting invitations to attend our serious theatres, asking querulously, "Why should we be interested in seeing plays in a language we don't understand?"

But they did like us, their strange "in-laws" of their second home. How well they liked us may be gathered from an incident one night in New Haven. The play was "Tsar Fyodor." Stanislavsky was not supposed to be in the cast at all. But when the curtain rose on the second act, those who were familiar with his gigantic frame and imposing bearing recognized him at once in the gorgeous robes of the high priest. The part has no lines; it is often played by a super. Stanislavsky as a super! For the first time in the history of the theatre, he had chosen to sink his identity and to forego the moving qualities of his wonderful voice in order to pay tribute to a community which, he felt, represented the best in American culture.

The influence of the Art Theatre on our own stage, too, is a matter that has little to do with statistics. It is perhaps too soon even yet to appraise that influence. But from the early furore of its discovery, from those Friday matinees attended by hundreds of actors who came, curious and unconvinced,

THE GODFATHER OF THE RUSSIAN THEATRE IN AMERICA AND
ITS PATRIARCH

Morris Gest Greets Constantin Stanislavsky on Board the *Majestic* on the Arrival
of the Moscow Art Theatre for Its First Season in America, January, 1923

THE MOSCOW ART THEATRE IN AMERICA

The Company in Front of Jolson's Fifty-Ninth Street Theatre, New York, 1923

(Left to right) Vadim Shveruhovitch, Ivan Gremislavsky, Vladimir Yershoff, Nina Litovtseva, Alexander Koiransky, Boris Dobronravoff, Akim Tamiroff, Peter Baksheieff, Alexei Bondirieff, Anna Phaleieva, ―――, Mihail Phaleieff, Anna Bodulina, Ivan Lazarieff, Ivan Gudkoff, Mihail Tarhanoff, Vassily Katchaloff, Lydia Korenieva, Giorgi Burdzhaloff, Maria Nikolaieva, Maria Uspenskaya, Varvara Bulgakova, Alla Tarasova, ―――, William H. Oviatt, Ripsime Tamantsova, Leonid D., Leonidoff, Nikolai Podgorny, Olga Knipper-Tche-hova, Constantin Stanislavsky, Morris Gest, Alexander Vishnevsky, Ivan Moskvin, Vladimir Gribunin, and Olga Bokshanskaya and departed humble or, like John Barrymore, remained to kiss Moskvin's hand and write to Gest thanking him for "the most amazing experience I have ever had by a million miles in the theatre"—from those emotional intoxications to the sober judgments of prolonged acquaintance and aftermath is a far step. That the Moscow Art Theatre survived the ordeal of extended and intimate contact is the best proof of the soundness of its achievement, the best witness to the title deed of its second home. As one who may be prejudiced by years of association with its work, I prefer to let others crystallize, as well as a short perspective permits, the residue to date of this second-cousin from Muscovy.

For example, Norman Hapgood has written : "How many times, since Stanislavsky first came over, I have read in one newspaper or another that such or such a play was acted up to the standard of the Moscow Art Theatre. The absurdity of the criticism is readily forgiven in view of the desire it shows in the critic to praise general balance of acting, and in view of the rising stage requirements that it accompanies."

Again, in the text accompanying Boris Grigorieff's "Visages de Russie," a gallery, for the most part, of the Art Theatre, Clare Sheridan writes : "In reviewing world conditions today one cannot ignore the Russian movement. It is one of the great historical phenomena that are making an indelible impression in the East, as well as in the West. On the American continent this influence is like a great tidal wave. The result of economic, political and social upheaval, the Russian movement, however, has divorced itself from politics. It is a movement of art, philosophy and Slavic culture. Too robust, too vital, too primitive to suffer ex-

[27]

tinction, it is imposing itself and its Russian conception of life upon the rest of the civilized world. The Russians are not consciously imposing this movement any more than the other nations are consciously being imposed upon, but it is nevertheless happening. . . . The great phenomenon of this wave of Russianism is its effect on New York. It is true that New York is not America, but New York is the nerve center of America. What begins in New York will in time radiate and penetrate through the great New Continent. America is deeply emotional, and that is perhaps one of the reasons why the best that Russia can give is being so genuinely appreciated by Americans. . . . The winter of 1923 culminated in the most triumphant success of the Moscow Art Theatre. Russian faces and Russian names became familiar and endeared to the American public. A people who had been regarded as superficial, spoilt and impatient came in crowds to the Russian Theatre, sat through hours of Russian performances of which they understood not a word, and that had no music, almost no stage setting, and no great variety of scenes to alleviate them! Instead of talking between acts, Americans were intent upon their translations. Stanislavsky had dominated them, and they had accepted it."

The cultured, non-professional viewpoint is thus expressed by the novelist, Henry James Forman: "Briefly then, what the players of the Moscow Art Theatre have done for us of the general public is to give us a broader sense of the possibilities of the theatre, a more quickened sense of consistently fine acting and the possibilities of a great and perfectly selected and trained stock company. A great stock company we shall surely have one day and the Moscow players have

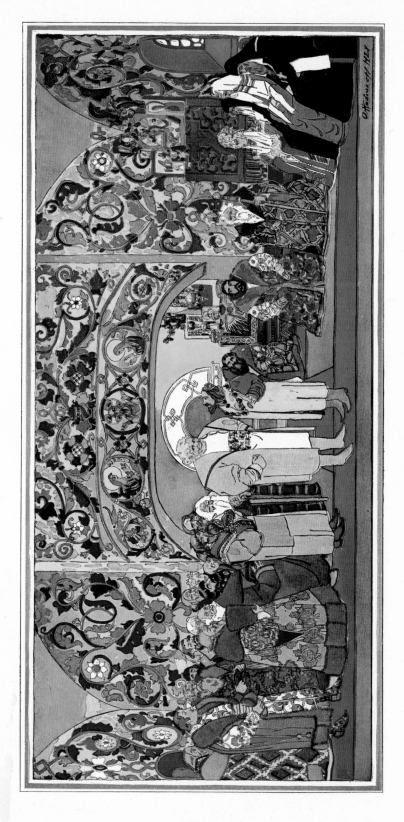

THE SCENE THAT ANNOUNCED THE MOSCOW ART THEATRE TO AMERICA

The Setting for the First Act in the Kremlin Palace in Count Alexei Tolstoy's Historical Tragedy, "Tsar Fyodor Ivanovitch."
A Painting by Andrei Hudiakoff after the Design by Victor Simoff and Nokolai Kruimoff.

hastened its advent. Also, they have brought us a deeper sense of reality on the stage. And, by no means least, they have introduced us into the treasury of the writings of Tchehoff—one of the greatest writers of all times. By us, I mean a very considerable section of the public. Any one of these services would have been of signal importance. All of them together form a combination that no visiting troupe of actors has ever brought us before."

And finally, from the theatre itself, let me summon Kenneth Macgowan: "We needed two lessons in regard to acting, and the Moscow Art Theatre brought us both. It showed us how fine and how interesting can be the actor's art when he tries to create varied characters—young and old, comic and tragic, mercurial and sluggard—instead of end-lessly repeating the pleasant exploitation of his own per-sonality. We saw the actor as the servant of character. The dramatist is its servant, and so is life. This lesson is one that we might have learned from other players from abroad or from some of the actors of our Yiddish theatres. But the Moscow Art Theatre company—fruit of a quarter century of conscious effort towards this goal—brought the perfect demonstration.

"The second lesson was how this fullness of impersonation and perfection of the actor's art could be accomplished—the machinery with which a genius like that of Stanislavsky and of Dantchenko could make such acting. This lesson, this machinery, is nothing more than the repertory company. Any large body of acting of true distinction is impossible unless a company of players work together season after season on a group of worthy plays."

That we are due for a second course in these same lessons at the hands of the Art Theatre's Musical Studio is the natural corollary to the fact that the Studio is inheritor and practitioner of the same methods and traditions that rule its parent, as I shall explain in Chapter V. There also, and in Chapter XII, I shall forecast the Musical Studio's possible influences on our lyric stage. The sponsorship of Morris Gest for this new visitor, the result of over two years of negotiation, is conceivably bringing him nearer to emulation of his earliest preceptor, Oscar Hammerstein; and the Moscow Art Theatre's further tenancy of its second home may thus prove to have even deeper implications for our operatic halls than it has already had for our dramatic stage.

So much for the immediate future. In the distance, I foresee, with Nemirovitch-Dantchenko, an intimate and intricate comity between the theatres of Russia and America. Hard as it is to believe, we have scarcely tapped the dramatic treasury of Russia. We may not yet be ready for everything her stages have developed. But each new visitor prepares the way for the next. The difficulty of cultivating this phase of the Theatre International to its full possibilities, as the co-founder of the Art Theatre well understands, lies in the great risks involved in individual and unrelated tours. One may reap glory and a fortune; another prove a fiasco. One may be timed at the psychological moment; another may be too early or too late. The policy of *laissez-faire* in such a case is wasteful.

Therefore, Nemirovitch-Dantchenko proposes the organization of a Russian-American Theatrical Foundation which will coördinate the forces of finance and intelligence, cut

THE LAST ACT OF "TSAR FYODOR IVANOVITCH"

Scene before the Cathedral in Count Alexei Tolstoy's Historical Tragedy, Which Served Not Only for the Art Theatre's Debut in 1898 but also for the Premiere of the American Engagement, January 8, 1923

THE TRIBUTE OF THE AMERICAN STAGE TO MOSCOW'S ESTHETIC AMBASSADORS

The Reception on the Stage of Jolson's Fifty-Ninth Street Theatre after the First Friday Matinee of "Tsar Fyodor Ivanovitch," January 12, 1923

(Left to right, front row) Mihail Dalmatoff, of Balieff's Chauve-Souris; Laurette Taylor; Ivan Moskvin, as Tsar Fyodor; Lenore Ulrich;
David Warfield; Constantin Stanislavsky; Morris Gest; Ethel Barrymore; Yvonne George and Julia Hoyt.
(Left to right, rear, from center) Alexander Vishnevsky, as Boris Godunoff; Olga Knipper-Techiehova, as the Tsarina Irina; Jobyna Howland;
Brandon Tynan and McKay Morris.

risks, apportion profits and losses and eliminate esthetic and
monetary waste. A triple secretariat—financial, literary and
executive—would suffice for administering such a Foundation, he thinks. And the unselfish vision which he brings
to the project is evident from the fact that he cites not only
his own theatre and its several branches, but the rival
Kamerny Theatre and the State Opera and Ballet as potential
candidates for consideration by this Foundation.

As I see it, however, one prohibitive flaw prevents the in-
auguration of such an international trust at the present time.
Free esthetic intercourse between nations, like unhampered
trade, presupposes untrammeled diplomatic relationships.
Until the political barriers between Russia and America are
cleared away, the Russian Theatre is likely to be compelled
to use its second home only when chance paves the way for
a visit.

CHAPTER III

DICTATORSHIP VS. COÖPERATION

HEAT, $11,000; light, $16,000. These items, picked at random from the Moscow Art Theatre's budget for last season, hint rather broadly at one of the reasons why the theatre's celebrated coöperative administration has been temporarily abandoned in favor of a rigid dictatorship. Whereas the Russian capital used to pay about half what we do for the same commodities and services, today the ratio is two to four or more times our own. In other words, although the ruble is at par in international exchange, its purchasing power inside Russia is only from 12½ per cent to 25 per cent of what it was formerly. In such an economic emergency, of course, one hand—if it be the right hand!—can guard the treasury more closely and make it work more effectively than a committee can. In such an emergency, particularly if the emergency be political and social as well as economic, questions of policy have to be settled on the spur of the moment. The committee talks; the dictator acts. Autocracy is the toll freedom pays for efficiency in a storm.

Apart from the general national emergency, however, the Art Theatre has been confronted suddenly with a crisis in its own affairs, an expansion of its activities and interests similar to that which a business partnership encounters on branching out into export trade. At any given moment the governing council may be split, with the majority of its members on the other side of the world, out of touch with conditions on the home stage and powerless to render intelligent decisions with regard to personnel, repertory and administration. Then, too, the Art Theatre's expansion at home has been so rapid and has become so intricate that the town meeting idea is both economically and artistically cumbersome and wasteful, at least until the new lines are clearly drawn and firmly established. In this connection, it is well to remember that, although operating on an annual budget like our own institutional theatres, the Art Theatre has no subscription list and is dependent on the unorganized support of the public—a support which has never failed but which can be scanned and estimated better from one commanding watch-tower than from twenty.

The old Moscow Art Theatre with a single company, content to confine itself to a single stage and a compact public, is a thing of the past. The first move toward a cleavage into several stages came with the founding of the First Studio over a decade ago. By 1916 the Second Studio had appeared. The Spring of 1920 saw the birth of the Musical Studio of Nemirovitch-Dantchenko. And the Autumn of 1921 added the Third and the Fourth Studios. In like manner, the rudiments of a world audience were acquired, modestly and by sheer accident, when in 1919 about a third of the dramatic company, playing a guest engagement in Harkoff, got cut off by the White armies and for three years wandered and acted in exile from Constantinople to Stockholm. Inside of still another year, the full force of the theatre had traveled as far as Chicago with less agitation than the old annual trips to Petersburg required. The tour of the

[33]

Musical Studio is the natural next step, the confirmation of the theatre's world importance and world function.

It was a frank recognition that these issues had reached the critical stage, therefore, which induced Nemirovitch-Dantchenko to cable in the late Winter of 1924 to his associates, then in this country, suggesting that they grant him dictatorial powers. To accede meant waiving, for the time at least, the admirable coöperative regulations which had been adopted in 1917 on the basis of twenty years experience. The details of those regulations—division of authority among the General Meeting, including all stockholders; the Council, in charge of all productions; and the Direction, in control of administration—I explained at length in "The Russian Theatre." The papers of incorporation were printed entire in the October, 1920, issue of *Theatre Arts Magazine*. I shall not stop here to reëxamine them. These statutes still stand as a model form of government for a self-contained institutional theatre operating under stable social and economic conditions.

Moreover, they still represent Nemirovitch-Dantchenko's own goal in theatre policy. As Yury Soboleff says in the final chapter of his illuminating biography of the co-founder of the Art Theatre:

"It seems to him that the ideal form of organization would be the creation of such an association, built on a coöperative basis, as would have no shareholding capitalists and would enlist all those associated with the theatre as shareholders—all the artists, the entire administration, all the employees and the technical and working personnel.

[34]

"To carry out such a plan would mean for Nemirovitch-Dantchenko to complete the circle of his ideas and dreams of a *new* theatre—new in its artistic tasks and in the external form of its organization, in which all his conscious life had been passed, in which all that nourished his creative powers would be expressed and in which all that sums up his personality would be disclosed."

Regret that this ideal dream had to be laid aside for the time being, deferred Nemirovitch-Dantchenko's appeal to his comrades until postponement was no longer a virtue. Regret likewise saddened those comrades in their decision to accede to the request. But, led by Stanislavsky himself, they sank personal prerogatives for the sake of the theatre, as so many individual artists had done in refusing to be lured from its ranks by offers of ten-fold salary, and unanimously voted Nemirovitch-Dantchenko dictator. Although it may not have been a conscious motive, there is every reason to believe that the coöperative body was spurred to its decision by observation of the efficient fruits of centralized power in American business and in the American theatre.

In any case, the opening of the new season in the fall of 1924, with all the theatre's forces reunited in Moscow, saw the application of the new regime with the results I have outlined in the first chapter—three stages and four companies, all answerable to the new dictator, except that Stanislavsky stands independent of the hegemony as adviser to the School, where he has an absolutely free hand to experiment with his system of dramatic interpretation, which he sketched so vividly in "My Life in Art" and to which he intends to devote an entire new volume.

The application of this new regime, with the erection of the old First Studio into a full-fledged theatre in its own right, the consolidation of the tractable elements of the Second, Third and Fourth Studios into the new Studio, and the secession of those who had lost sympathy with the Art Theatre's ideals, as well as a resume of the years of world-wandering on the part of the Dramatic Company—all these developments were amusingly satirized by V. Tchernoyaroff in a recent issue of *Zhizn Iskusstva ("The World of Art")*. The author takes the Russian initials of the theatre M. H. A. T. (*Moskovsky Hudozhestvenny Academitchesky Teatr*—Moscow Art Academic Theatre), and weaves the following tale of the domestic crisis in the Mhat household:

"The Mhat family was respectable and patriarchal. The father (Stanislavsky) devoted himself, with the aid of all available textbooks on psychology, to educating his children in accordance with his own system. The mother, whose maiden name was Nemirovitch-Dantchenko, took care of the house. If the couple ever quarreled, it was only for a short time, but they never did their washing in public. The children were neat, well-groomed, well-bred, and obedient; they never spoke in the presence of their elders. Everyone envied this family.

" 'Here is an example to follow!'

" 'An ideal family!'

"The children were pampered, hugged, petted, and plied with candy.

" 'A living image of the father!'

" 'That is what system can do!'

"But all of a sudden, just before the silver jubilee, con-

[36]

flicts arose. The characters of the couple began to draw apart.

"Tastes and habits shared for twenty-five years began to change. The mother began to dance and to sing gay operatic motives, recalled from her youth, and in general conducted herself rather frivolously. The father solemnly occupied himself with cosmic problems and started to wander unrepentant about the world. The parents separated. The children were left without attention. The mother's mind was bent upon one thing—to cut her capers as facetiously as possible and yet not without a certain decency, as befits a mother of a family. The father wrote from time to time, sending picture postcards.

"Two years passed. Infatuations were over. The mother became more serious and began to see in 'Carmen' a sex tragedy. The father grew tired of his wanderings about the world. And after an exchange of letters, the couple decided to reunite.

"The reunion was touching. In order to please the mother and be the better understood, the father sang from 'The Chimes of Normandy':

> "This world three times I traveled 'round,
> Quite brave I learned to be.
> That life right well agreed with me;
> To ladies German, Spanish, American
> I gave my love; they promised me
> The idols of my love to be."

"The mother sang sourly from 'Yevgeny Onyegin,' which the father had always greatly admired:

" 'Habits are given us by the Lord to take the place of happiness.'

"And so the parents made up. Having made up, they decided together to devote themselves to their children. The mother began to complain:

" 'It is simply impossible to get along with them. No sooner had you departed than they turned their caps aslant. They became mischievous. "We," they shouted, "are futurists." Just think of it! Where on earth did they get that word? They made strange acquaintances. They brought in a houseful of friends. And all of them were without breeding or social standing.'

"The eldest son was called. He stepped in, sat down in an armchair and asked in a bass voice:

" 'May one smoke?'

"The father clasped his hands!

" 'You smoke?'

" 'Yes, I smoke. I have now in my pocket, father, a diploma of graduation. I ask you, therefore, not to give me any advice, and not to interfere in my private life. It is enough for me to be laughed at by my friends. I have my own demands, and you continue keeping me in the nursery. I am asking, father, for a separate room. I am now engaged in self-development and have given up all youthful trifles. I am studying "Hamlet." '

"The father was delighted.

" 'That is very good! My innermost dream was always to be an older comrade to my son—to explain, guide, instruct——'

"The son cast a gloomy glance at his father.

" 'You had better stop that, father. I have already passed my examinations and do not intend to study any longer. As to "Hamlet"—that is a trifle. Once—and over with. I cultivate it instead of a mustache—that everyone may see that I am mature.'

" 'I should like to see what you would do without your father!'

" 'I will show you.'

"The parents exchanged glances:

" 'What a dunce he has grown up to be! All right—you shall have a separate room!' "

In turn, the younger children were called in, according to Tchernoyaroff, and each was chastised, warned, forgiven or disowned, until the household of the family Mhat was set in order once more.

Joking aside, the task of reorganization was not so simple. Hours of patient consultation were required to coördinate the Art Theatre's human resources and set the huge machine working smoothly, with its wheels within wheels. To this problem, the Dramatic Company with its associated Studio and School contributed a quota of over three hundred people; the Musical Studio, nearly 150; and the Moscow Art Theatre, Second, nearly two hundred—a total personal roster of over 650.

To visualize the processes of this great human machine and to understand the relationships of its parts would be hopelessly confusing without a chart, a family tree. With such a chart as I have provided from data obtained through Sergei Berthensson in the Art Theatre's offices, little more need be said. Examination, however, reveals several significant facts. The organization of the Dramatic Company's activities, although ultimately answerable to the Director, is more intricate and mutually responsible than that of the other companies, due to the fact that its leading members have had years of experience in self-government under the old coöperative regime. The Musical Studio, on the other hand, is accountable directly to Nemirovitch-Dantchenko through his vice-regent, Berthensson; while the Moscow Art Theatre, Second, has entrusted itself wholly to its outstanding genius, Mihail Tchehoff, nephew of the playwright, over whom the Director-in-Chief stands in a largely advisory capacity.

The impression you gain in Moscow is that the regime of the dictator is only temporary, that it will pass with the return of economic stability and normal foreign relations. Considering the material and geographical expansion of the theatre's life in the last five years, however, I doubt whether it will ever be possible again to revert to the loose coöperative form of administration. But, just as the statutes embodying that form will always serve as a model for self-contained institutional theatres, so the hierarchy set forth in the chart of the new regime will repay study on the part of a many-sided and far-flung theatrical group. It is a strange paradox that out of the Russia that is supposed to have no experience or instinct in the art of government, should have come two such sharply contrasting prototypes of theatrical organization, each admirably suited to the exigencies it has to meet.

CHAPTER IV

The Dramatic Company

WHAT lay ahead of the Dramatic Company of the Moscow
Art Theatre on its return home was a matter of grave con-
cern during its last days in this country. I remember the
air of uncertainty and dread that pervaded a talk I had in
March, 1924, after a rehearsal in Poli's Theatre, Washington, with Sergei Berthensson, business manager of the company in America and latterly Nemirovitch-Dantchenko's
right-hand man, not only as executive in charge of the personnel of the Dramatic Company but his viceroy in the
Musical Studio. The Council had just signed its own ab-
dication and ratified the dictatorship, and everyone in the
company suspected that there might be some secret and
sinister emergency behind Nemirovitch-Dantchenko's request
which he dared not divulge in cable or letter. No Russian
feels happy, or at any rate natural, I sometimes think, unless
he has a sense of foreboding. As someone put it not long
ago, the motto of the race is: "Thank God, I'm miserable!"

As a matter of fact, no mysterious crisis existed, although
problems were plenty. Reunited on the home stage in Sep-
tember, the world-wanderers faced, among other issues, a
straitened economy and a circumscribed repertory. The first
of these they met, as I have told, by accepting reduced
salaries. In solving the second, they had fortunate recourse

[41]

to the theatre's varied past until new productions in tune with the times could be prepared. That the repertory would be scrutinized by the Soviet, they knew before leaving us. Just what would fall under the ban they were not aware. Nevertheless, they summoned courage to announce the season's plans in bidding us farewell: Revivals of Griboyedoff's "The Sorrows of the Spirit" *("Gore ot Uma"),* Gogol's "The Inspector General" and Pushkin's "The Stone Guest."

Tchehoff, they suspected, would be proscribed. And he was—for no reason that anyone but the most bigoted social doctrinaire could understand. The author of "The Cherry Orchard" would probably smile his inscrutable smile at the thought that anything he ever wrote could jeopardize anything in life but sloth and intolerance and inhumanity. The technical charge against him is that he and his characters are "bourgeois." But with all his penetrating and ruthless exposure of their foibles, he is far from being an apologist for bourgeois ideals.

Work was rushed, therefore, on the revival of Gogol's "The Inspector General." Meanwhile, what remained of the American repertory that would survive the censor's ordeal? "The Lower Depths"?

— Satisfactory.

"The Death of Pazuhin"?

— Harmless.

"Tsar Fyodor"?

— Once a month might not prove dangerous.

But how fill a repertory at this rate? And besides, in spite of the hundreds of performances of this production and Moscow's familiarity with it for twenty-seven years, it would command all the interest of novelty through the fact that Katchaloff, over whom as rival to Moskvin men fought in the Jolson Theatre lobby, had never before played Fyodor in the Kremlin City.

— Very well, once a week until "The Sorrows of the Spirit" is ready.

Incidentally, "The Sorrows of the Spirit" wasn't ready until Spring, so Katchaloff's saintly weakling is by now as familiar—and as much the subject of heated controversy —in Moscow as in Gotham!

Then there was the question of "The Blue Bird." After seven years of toleration under the Soviet, Maeterlinck's fantasy was finally outlawed because it is a fairy story. But the foregathering of the youngsters to revel in its whimsy and beauty every Sunday afternoon was a substantial and dependable item in the theatre's budget. Nemirovitch-Dantchenko, therefore, appealed directly to Anatoly V. Lunatcharsky, Kommissar of Education and, ex officio, overlord of Russia's playhouses.

— Oh, well, go ahead and play it until someone objects. It's really a classic, you know.

Classic, by the way, is the convenient loop-hole by which the Minister of Education and the Fine Arts has managed to save from destruction, at the hands of more ruthless members of the Government, many of Russia's artistic treasures, including the golden double eagles atop the Kremlin Cathedrals!

"The Inspector General" had already been introduced into the repertory by the time I reached Moscow and had scored a triumph, with Moskvin as the town-bailiff and the young

[43]

Tchehoff as the nonchalant impostor, Hlestyakoff. Tche-hoff's "Hamlet" at the Moscow Art Theatre, Second, how-ever, had thrown Gogol's comedy into temporary eclipse while I was there, for the burden of both rôles in the same week was too great for his intense but frail powers.

The revival of "The Sorrows of the Spirit" kindled anew the old fires of coöperative creation, for Stanislavsky and Nemirovitch-Dantchenko resumed their original posts of co-regisseurs—the first instance in many years of their active collaboration on the same production. The premiere did not take place until Spring, after the Art Theatre's cus-tom of deferring public performance until everything is ready, no matter how long it takes. But rehearsals were in an advanced state in December, and I shall never forget the warm and hearty glow that suffused the entire company at the sight of these two old war-horses directing rehearsals side by side on the stage, first one and then the other break-ing into a bit of pantomime or dialogue as example to the players. Contrasting with this note of enthusiasm, however, was the regret everyone felt that mature years had compelled Katchaloff to surrender the rôle of Tchatsky to the brilliant young player from the old Third Studio, Zovadsky. Every-where throughout the theatre, from artists in their own mature prime, like Olga Knipper-Tchehova, to those on their artistic threshold, like Alla Tarasova, I heard the same ex-pression: "That is the tragedy of the actor. When he learns fully and richly how to play a rôle, he is too old for it."

The first choice of a new production fell on "Puga-tchovshchina" ("The Times of Pugatchoff"), a heroic and

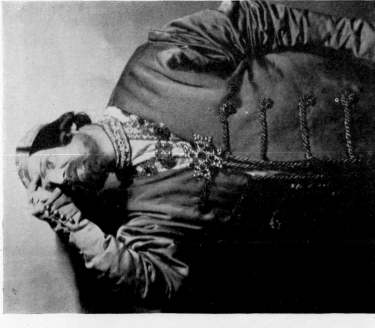

Bruguière, New York

THE TSAR OF IVAN MOSKVIN IS HUMAN AND NEUROTIC

Atwell, Chicago

VASSILY KATCHALOFF MAKES FYODOR A SAINTLY WEAKLING

RIVALS IN THE TITLE ROLE OF COUNT ALEXEI TOLSTOY'S "TSAR FYODOR IVANOVITCH"

Bruguiere, New York

As the Pilgrim, Luka,
In Gorky's "The Lower Depths"

Marcia Stein, New York

In Life

IVAN MOSKVIN—HIGH COMEDIAN

As Yepihodoff
In Tchehoff's "The Cherry Orchard"

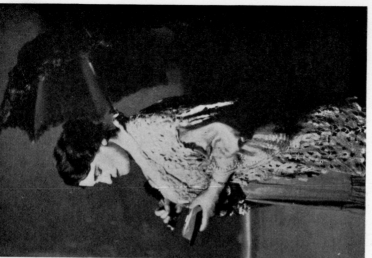

Bruguiere, New York

AS MADAME RANEVSKAYA

In Tchehoff's "The Cherry Orchard"

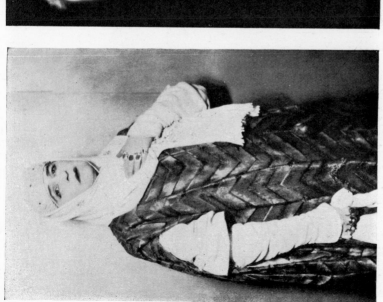

Marcia Stein, New York

IN LIFE

Bruguiere, New York

AS THE TSARINA IRINA

In Tolstoy's "Tsar Fyodor Ivanovitch"

OLGA KNIPPER-TCHEHOVA IN PERSON AND IN HER FAVORITE ROLES

Gilbert René, Paris

LEONID M. LEONIDOFF

As Dmitry in Dostoievsky's "The Brothers Karamazoff"

ALEXANDER VISHNEVSKY

As the Stolid Tatar in Gorky's "The Lower Depths"

Gilbert René, Paris

VASSILY LUZHSKY

As Fyodor Pavlovitch, the Father, in Dostoievsky's "The Brothers Karamazoff"

THREE MAJOR FIGURES IN THE DRAMATIC COMPANY

spectacular drama of a celebrated peasant uprising under Catherine the Great, written by Constantin Trenyeff. In history Pugatchoff was a hideous and bloodthirsty ruffian who pretended to be the late Tsar Peter III, victim of Catherine's ambition; who took advantage of the peasant unrest attendant upon the Tsarina's costly foreign wars, marshalled a guerilla army of muzhiks and disaffected Cossacks and spread terror throughout the Volga basin for a year. In his play, Trenyeff has used his history freely, elevating the peasant mob and the Cossacks into the rôles of heroes protesting against oppression. It is easy to see, therefore, why the play has passed the censor. Incidentally, the Government may have in mind, through this salutary example, the purpose of forestalling the appearance of a false Tsar Nicholas II, for Russian history is dotted with instances of pretenders to the throne, when the monarch disappeared under mysterious circumstances.

Just as in "Tsar Fyodor," the Art Theatre approached the task of recreating this distant episode in Russian history with a thoroughness which stopped at no pains. The author was summoned from his home in Simferopol in the Crimea to assist the regisseurs, Leonidoff and Luzhsky, and to instruct the players in the difficult dialect of the Cossacks of the Don and the Dnieper. Quite characteristic, too, was the decision to forego the sentimental satisfaction of giving the premiere on the one hundred and fiftieth anniversary of Pugatchoff's execution, January 23, 1925, for the simple reason that the production was not ready and will not be until after these lines reach print. In America it would have been hurried through and presented, ready or no.

[45]

The three performances of the Dramatic Company which I saw last winter confirmed judgments I have already expressed: that "The Lower Depths" is the greatest play in the repertory of the Art Theatre, if not the greatest from the pen of a modern writer, and that its performance is the most profoundly moving in the orchestrated acting of its ensemble; that Katchaloff's Tsar Fyodor is even finer, subtler and more spiritual than Moskvin's splendid interpretation; and that "The Blue Bird," as Stanislavsky has visualized it, is the supreme height of imaginative beauty in the modern theatre.

To devote three evenings out of twelve days to familiar productions may seem strange, but the opportunity to do so came largely through finding most of the other theatres in Moscow deadly dull, whereupon I hopped in a droshky and hurried back "home." I saw "The Lower Depths," however, the Monday night of my arrival, when all the theatres are supposed to be dark; but on this particular evening the Art Theatre was giving its annual gift performance to selected members of the Red Army. It was an imposing sight— that row upon row of trim uniforms and determined young faces drawn from a melting pot almost as heterogeneous racially as our own. And on the other side of the footlights, there was Moskvin as Luka, Tarasova as Nastya, Vishnevsky as the Tatar, Burdzhaloff as Kostilyoff, Alexandroff as the Actor, Shevtchenko as Vassilisa, Gribunin as Miedviedieff, and so forth—all of them as familiar and endeared to New York and a dozen other American cities as they are to Moscow.

In Moscow where the barbaric splendors of the Kremlin

are as familiar as the Woolworth Tower is to us, I missed, somehow, the electric thrill that used to run through each American audience at the rise of the curtain on "Tsar Fyódor" and remained as a kind of hushed wonder throughout the evening. Since I had seen it first in New York, the sight of it in Moscow took me back home just as surely as "The Lower Depths" in America always used to spirit me off to Moscow and the first days of the Revolution. It was good to see that the handsome and towering Yershoff had been rewarded for turning a deaf ear to fabulous motion picture offers from Hollywood by the opportunity to play— and play regally—the sinister rôle of Boris Godunoff.

As for "The Blue Bird," it would be the apex of loquacity to try to add anything to my chapter in "The Russian Theatre." Many times since I wrote that chapter in the glow of first acquaintance, I have said to myself, *"Can anything in the theatre be as ravishingly beautiful as that?"* But, despite my doubts, distance only doubled enchantment. I hesitated to see it again, for fear of breaking the spell. But curiosity got the better of me—and rewarded me for my temerity. For I hereby not only repeat but underscore all that I wrote before. If the Dramatic Company ever returns to its second home, "The Blue Bird" must head its repertory.

CHAPTER V

The Musical Studio of Vladimir Nemirovitch-Dantchenko

Talent, it appears, runs not only in families but in institutions. We Americans are too young a nation to provide proof of that fact. Until very recent years, our arts, and particularly our theatre, neglected the institutional form altogether. The individualism of the pioneer persisted. But there is no other possible explanation for the vitality which the Comédie Française, for instance, has disclosed in generation after generation. The latest of the great institutional theatres of Europe to add its testimony in proof of this law of artistic heredity is the Moscow Art Theatre, whose Musical Studio was founded only five years ago by Vladimir Nemirovitch-Dantchenko. Quickly developing into a most precocious youngster, this lyric daughter of sober parents already challenges comparison with them at home and abroad.

The birth, rapid growth and sudden accession to world fame of this new company is a most effective answer to a question which many people asked during the sojourn of the Art Theatre's Dramatic Company with us. That question was: Is this wonderful institution doomed, with the inevitable passing of time, to disappear, leaving only memory of its achievements and the stimulus of its example? Not only those who were skeptical about the Russians, but also their stanchest friends, asked this question and found no evidence for a hopeful answer. Norman Hapgood, for instance, put the question thus:

"The technique of the Russians grew out of a flaming ideal, and would never have been born without that flame. Will the younger members carry the standard as high as Stanislavsky, Katchaloff, Knipper, Moskvin and the rest of the company's first line? From 1914 life in Russia, even more than elsewhere, has been turbulent. Also Stanislavsky and Nemirovitch-Dantchenko, his fellow manager, had the momentum of their own creative idea and the long sacrifice for its fulfillment. Ten years from now we shall know whether the energy and the vision of the younger artists are worthy of their inheritance."

As Moscow already knows and as we shall know soon, the answer has come more promptly. Mr. Hapgood and the rest who doubted, whether gladly or reluctantly, underestimated the power of institutional heredity. The spirit of the Moscow Art Theatre has been born anew in its lyric daughter. In fact, the question was answered over in Moscow before we in America had an opportunity to ask it. With passing time and successive productions, the answer becomes more emphatic. For while environment and natural development sharpen the contrasts with the parent, they also intensify the kinship in spirit—in institutions as well as in men.

Suppose we examine briefly, for the purposes of getting acquainted, the points of family similarity and personal divergence. How does the Musical Studio resemble its sober parent? How does it differ? Like the Dramatic Company, it is a product of the most vigorous standards of thorough rehearsal, of repertory presentation, of scorn for the star system, of rotation of rôles and of inner psychological truth in the interpretation of those rôles—standards which have been extended by Nemirovitch-Dantchenko to apply to the singing voice and the plastic body. The influence of these common precepts has been intensified, of course, by close association with the atmosphere in which they were conceived and perfected, for the stage of the Moscow Art Theatre has been the home of the Musical Studio since its foundation. For two years before the Dramatic Company came to America, the Musical Studio shared with it the repertory; for two more years it held the fort alone under the keen spur of responsibility for the family name; and last winter it resumed the rôle of collaborator.

On the other hand, there are the essential variations connoted by the title. The art of the Musical Studio is lyric instead of dramatic. Rather, lyric *and* dramatic. Its company is composed of actor-singers, or, if you prefer, of singing-actors. Its repertory is one in which the singing voice obliterates the barriers to enjoyment of a performance in a foreign tongue. The daughter thereby is not false to the parent, but has merely mastered a further esthetic means of expression. There are other differences, each naturally derivative from this lyric character. For one thing, accustomed as we are to the dignity and sedateness of the Dramatic Company, the Musical Studio will surprise us by the fire and the impetuosity and the virility of its youth. It is youth that sings, and these young people are eager, enthusiastic, gay, full of the spirit of life as none but Russians

[50]

know how to be full. Then, too, music not only admits freer, more symbolic, more rhythmic, less naturalistic stage settings and expression of character; it demands them. Nevertheless, despite these points of divergence, the Musical Studio has every right to use the jealously guarded insignia of the Sea-Gull. For all its individuality, it is a chip of the old block!

Like everything new and strange, the Musical Studio met determined opposition at its birth. Conservative critics and patrons of the theatre in the Russian capital resented the fact that their favorite stage in its ripe maturity had chosen to become young again, to play the pioneer once more in the contemporary art of the theatre. They forgot, apparently, that it had been an artistic revolutionist itself in its youth, nearly a quarter of a century before. The Moscow Art Theatre, these esthetic fundamentalists insisted, had sold its birthright for a mess of popular pottage—for there was no denying the popularity of the new departure. They charged Nemirovitch-Dantchenko, therefore, with playing down to the new audience that had preëmpted the theatre under the Soviet, and they predicted the passing of this stage as a world-famous institution.

There was a measure of justification for the attitude of these dramatic fundamentalists. Nemirovitch-Dantchenko did have one practical eye to the current situation. The Dramatic Company of the theatre had been split in two in 1919, as I have told, by the virtual exile of over a third of its leading players. Something had to be done to fill the gap, and the Musical Studio would do it. Nemirovitch-Dantchenko was shrewd enough, too, to realize that the new

[51]

theatre audience would judge on its merits, without preconceptions, any experiment designed to reënforce the de-
pleted Dramatic Company on the home stage. Ever since
his youth, he had felt the lure of the lyric stage. Now
the time was ripe. Thus far, and thus far only, he was an
opportunist.

What Nemirovitch-Dantchenko's critics, like all fundamentalists, neglected to do was to visualize his ultimate goal,
to inquire into its implications, to search his deeper motives.
If they had done so, they would have found that the Musical
Studio was in reality not a betrayal of the traditions of the
Moscow Art Theatre but, on the contrary, a more complete
fulfillment of those traditions. Just because the lyric stage—
in Russia as in every other country today—was dying of dry
rot and of endless repetition of worn-out formulas, was no
reason why lyric drama should be considered an inferior
form of art.

To condemn lyric drama as beneath notice was, in the
opinion of Nemirovitch-Dantchenko, just like rejecting a
fine piece of machinery because the workmen had put it together clumsily. The several and separate parts existed in
superb perfection—world-famous orchestras, talented scenic
designers, able actors, soul-stirring voices, great masters of
the plastic human body, profound poets and composers and
their works since the beginning of time. You got a hint
of what might be attained whenever Chaliapin came on the
stage in "Boris." For a moment, all the wheels of the machine worked together, achieving a rhythm far more exalted
and all-inclusive than any merely spoken drama could hope to
produce. In other words, you had a glimpse of what

IN VIENNA, AT THE HOTEL BRISTOL, AUGUST, 1925

Morris Gest Receives from Nemirovitch-Danchenko the Permission of the Minister of Education, A. V. Lunatcharsky, for the Company to Leave Russia

IN BERLIN, AT THE HOTEL ADLON, AUGUST, 1923

The Project Was First Broached, Midway between the Two American Seasons of the Dramatic Company. (Left to right) Dr. Sergei Berthensson, Vladimir Nemirovitch-Dantchenko, Morris Gest, Dr. Leonid D. Leonidoff

TWO YEARS OF NEGOTIATION FOR THE MOSCOW ART THEATRE MUSICAL STUDIO

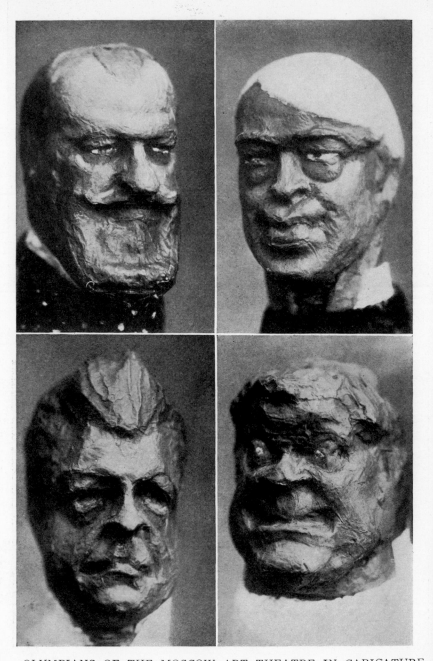

OLYMPIANS OF THE MOSCOW ART THEATRE IN CARICATURE

Comic Busts by Nikolai Andreieff in the Museum of the Art Theatre. (Above)
Vladimir Nemirovitch-Danchenko and Constantin Stanislavsky (below)
Vassily Luzhsky and Ivan Moskvin

Nemirovitch-Dantchenko likes to call the Synthetic Theatre
—a theatre in which all of the conceivable elements and
crafts have been fused into unity, not merely superimposed
one on another.

The vision of this Synthetic Theatre was one thing.
Goethe had sensed it vaguely at Weimar. Wagner had come
nearer to it at Bayreuth, defeating the full achievement of
his aims, probably, by trying to do everything himself and
by letting the orchestra run away with the other elements of
the music-drama, as we shall see more fully in Chapter XI.
Nemirovitch-Dantchenko, likewise, had cherished the dream
ever since his youthful days as a critic and connoisseur of
both music and drama. He had had his own discouragements, his own failures, in trying to bring the dream to life.
Invited a few years ago to the stage of the Great State
Theatre, the Metropolitan Opera House of Moscow, he had
tried to persuade mature singers to give up their artificial
traditions, their temperamental jealousies and their personal
prerogatives and to yield themselves into his hand for the
sake of a vivid and living operatic ensemble. But the artists,
no matter how good a will many of them had, were too old,
too set in their ways.

The crystallization of the vision, therefore, is another and
far more difficult thing. You can not eradicate from celebrated prima donnas and tenors the faults and false standards
ingrained by years of repetition. But you do not need a
company of celebrated names. You can not go out on the
street, even in Moscow where everyone seems to have a
passable singing voice, and gather in a whole company of
Chaliapins. But you don't need a whole company of Chalia-

pins. The esthetic formula underlying the genius of Chaliapin is the thing that counts: the actor who can sing, the
singer who can act. Let a regisseur with a vision of the
Synthetic Theatre build a company out of such units as
these, uncorrupted by the practice of false theories, and he
is well on the way toward the embodiment of his dream.

"Only within the walls of the Moscow Art Theatre," says
Nemirovitch-Dantchenko, "could I attain such results as I
had visualized. In another building, in any other theatre,
the task would have been much more difficult. Here the
atmosphere of triviality is an utter impossibility." And yet,
despite the assistance of this earnest atmosphere, the encouragement of this tradition for taking pains, the regisseur
realized that with his new venture he would have to fly in
the face of many of the theories which he had helped to work
out in practice within those walls, that he would have to
evolve new theories, new traditions, to meet new needs.

According to Sergei Berthensson, Nemirovitch-Dantchenko
saw his task and put the question that lay at the heart of it
in this way: "If a wonderful singer is not first of all an
actor, if he is not an artistic medium for the creation of a
dramatic image, participating in the dynamics of an operatic
production, if he is able only to sing wonderfully, then there
is no reason for him to don one costume or another, to put
on wigs, to paste on a beard, to take in his hand a sword, a
banner, a cup or a rope, or in general to attempt to resemble
a genuine dramatic actor, while he is not one. Such a singer
needs a low platform, a dress suit or any other costume,
just to make him *statuesque*. We should seek for an interesting oratorial or symphonic form for a group of such

singers. It is a different matter if the singing-actor re-animates the drama. Only such a one as this can create a performance instead of a concert.

"It would be the greatest mistake, and disastrous for the music, to construct an operatic performance according to the naturalistic methods of the drama. Here, specific approaches are necessary. For his main approach, his leading covenant, Nemirovitch-Dantchenko, as regisseur, observes what he calls 'the law of inner justification.' A singer must not, like a dramatic actor, live his rôle realistically. A singer can not cry because a sincere tear would contract his larynx; he can not laugh without risk of spoiling his tone. But with a flexible artistic fantasy, he can detect an inner problem, embracing the musical foundations of the subject matter, the psychological background and the plastic form. Without this 'inner justification,' all so-called 'play' results in nothing but stencils, frauds—all that which creates tasteless and unconvincing 'theatricality.'"

With these clear-cut conceptions of his problems, of the opportunities, the demands and the restrictions of the wholly new field he was entering at an age when most artists consider their creative career finished, Nemirovitch-Dantchenko set to work. In the Dramatic Company of the Moscow Art Theatre he found a young actress, Olga Baklanova, just turned twenty, who had thrilled her hearers vocally and dramatically on the parent stage in the rôles of Laura in Pushkin's "The Stone Guest," Sasha in Tchehoff's "Ivanoff" and Olga Petrovna in Turgenieff's "The Boarder"; and in the First Studio as Olivia in "Twelfth Night," Bertha in "The Cricket on the Hearth" and Lizzie (Sadie) in Berger's

"The Deluge." Her entry into the Art Theatre from a musical family was the result of examinations which she and only three others passed out of four hundred applicants.

In "The Russian Theatre" I wrote of her: "Somehow it is difficult to see how Baklanova's trenchant feeling and colorful methods will find full outlet in the restrained realism of the Art Theatre. But it may be that such as she will instill into it new life when it has run its course in its present mood." And that is exactly the function she has had the good fortune to serve while still well under thirty and still in full possession of the fiery talents of youth. For around her as a nucleus has been gathered a company of gifted young actor-singers whom the regisseur has taken, unspoiled and pliable, and molded into an ensemble that, in its more broadly-appealing field, rivals the Dramatic Company we already know. I shall not attempt here a further characterization of individual members of this ensemble, for the names of the most important will emerge in connection with their interpretation of the leading rôles in the chapters on the Musical Studio's several productions.

Lured by the reputation of the Moscow Art Theatre, these young people came from every profession. One left a railroad office, one was a soldier, another a farmer, another a secretary to an English oil company in Baku; still others were teachers, lawyers, students in religious and secular institutions. They came from almost every province of Russia. A register of eighteen of the most important members of the company shows six from Moscow, two from Kieff, one each from the cities of Kazan, Vladivostok, and Astrahan and one each from the Governments of Voroniezh,

Penza, Tula, Vladimir, Ufa, Smolensk, and Yekaterinoslav. Superimposed on a map with which we are more familiar than that of Russia, this roster represents a range north and south from Miami to Duluth and east and west from San Francisco to London!

Each of these youthful pilgrims had cherished dreams of the lyric stage—vain dreams as long as the established opera was not only dull and stilted but also cold to new blood. The summons of Nemirovitch-Dantchenko in the autumn of 1919 opened the doors of art and life to them. Rigorous vocal and dramatic tests weeded out the manifestly unfit. The remainder, whose youth and adaptability were as valuable assets as their talents for singing and acting, were formed into a studio. Vocal development and training in body plastic went hand in hand with instruction in acting according to the methods already tested by Stanislavsky and Nemirovitch-Dantchenko in the Art Theatre's Dramatic Studios.

To assist him in these courses of training and in direction, the regisseur built up little by little a staff in sympathy with his ideals. At the outset he summoned from the Theatre of Musical Drama in Petrograd the conductor and composer, Vladimir Bakaleynikoff. As chorus master and second conductor, he drafted Constantin Shvedoff simultaneously from the Moscow Touring Opera Company, another member of the younger musical generation who has made a name for himself as a composer. In the second season he induced one of the most experienced regisseurs on the Russian lyric stage, Vladimir Lossky, to undertake the rôle of Larivaudière in "The Daughter of Madame Angot" and that of the Viceroy in "La Périchole," besides entrusting him with heavy responsibilities in production. His other mainstay in production is Leonid Baratoff, a comedian of great resourcefulness and an able trainer in body plastic who has been associated with the Art Theatre since 1916 and who has devoted his talents to the Musical Studio since 1922.

Mindful that his protégés lacked experience at the start, the regisseur began with light opera, or opéra-comique. The choice fell on Lecocq's "The Daughter of Madame Angot," the libretto of which was adapted and revitalized with the aid of Mihail Galperin. And with this tale of the French Revolution, as inevitably seen through the eyes of the Russian, the Musical Studio opened its doors on May 16, 1920—a testimonial to the grit and stamina of Russian artists, for this was in the midst of the disturbed nation's most appalling famine year. Two seasons passed before the second production was ready, Offenbach's "La Périchole." The wonder is, not that the repertory was so slow in growing, but that artists, hungry and facing death, had the ambition and energy to make a single new production, let alone dream and put into effect the intricate mechanism of a wholly new company. At the premiere of "La Périchole," July 14, 1922, Moscow discovered that Nemirovitch-Dantchenko had been emboldened by his success with "Angot" and, again with the assistance of Galperin, had entirely remade the libretto in true keeping, as he saw it, with the spirit of the composer, who, like most of his fellows of the mid-nineteenth century, suffered from inferior literary collaboration.

In the third year, just after the Dramatic Company had rounded out its first season with us, the blustering and gro-

"CARMENCITA AND THE SOLDIER"

The Finale. A sketch by Andrei Hudiakoff after the setting by Isaac Rabinovitch

tesque old comedy of Aristophanes, "Lysistrata," had its premiere in Moscow, June 16, 1923, with unexpurgated text, with music in the Greek manner by the modern Russian composer, Gliere, and with the aid of a startling mechanical novelty in the form of a hitherto untried use of the revolving stage. The Musical Studio had "arrived" as an independent organization.

It came fully of age a year later, June 4, 1924—still during the absence of the Dramatic Company—when Nemirovitch-Dantchenko disclosed his wholly new version of the Bizet-Mérimée opera, "Carmen." Under title of "Carmencita and the Soldier," the thrilling and beloved score of Bizet was retained. The regisseur, however, found the Meilhac-Halévy libretto just as hopelessly artificial and false to Mérimée's story as Bizet himself had regarded it a half century ago. So he commissioned the Russian poet, Constantin Lipskeroff, to go directly back to the Mérimée story and make a new libretto. The result was a lyric drama, a lyric tragedy, as passionately intense, in point of story, of acting opportunity and of literary merit, as the famous score.

A fifth bill, "Love and Death," had its premiere at a single performance in June, 1925, before the company disbanded for the summer. It is made up of three short operas or lyric dramas, linked not only by a common source in Russia's greatest poet, Alexander Pushkin, but also by continuity of theme. To Americans, the item of outstanding interest in this bill will be "Aleko," by the great composer-pianist, Sergei Rachmaninoff, written before he became a world-figure, to a libretto by Nemirovitch-Dantchenko, then also young in the ways of fame. Other works still in the rehearsal stage, one of which may have its premiere on American soil, include Rebikoff's opera, "A Nobleman's Nest" (after the tale by Turgenieff), which the censor has prohibited in Moscow, and "Boris Godunoff," with Musorgsky's original score minus Rimsky-Korsakoff's prettifications. In this version, the first rehearsal of which I attended, the Russian people rather than the Tsar stand forth as the heroic center of the tragedy.

Of course, being only human in the first place and Russians in the second, the Musical Studio had to have a celebration on its fifth anniversary, May 16, 1925. Records totaled in that occasion show the following number of performances during the theatre's first half-decade:

"The Daughter of Madame Angot," 262.
"La Périchole," 125.
"Lysistrata," 113.
"Carmencita and the Soldier," 30.

Overshadowing this numerical record, of course, is the new company's leavening effect on Moscow's lyric stage. Other dramatic revolutionists, more insistent and strident, have swarmed Russian stages since the Revolution, but all of them put together have had less weight than the Art Theatre's Musical Studio in prying the established operatic stages from their dead routine.

That this company may conceivably give a healthy jolt to our own complacent lyric stage and its equally complacent audience, I shall attempt to show in Chapter XII. The Russians, as they reenter their second home, singing and

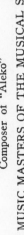

VLADIMIR BAKALEYNIKOFF
Conductor

Mishkin, New York

SERGEI RACHMANINOFF
Composer of "Aleko"

REINHOLD GLIÈRE
Composer of "Lysistrata" and "Cleopatra"

THE MUSIC MASTERS OF THE MUSICAL STUDIO

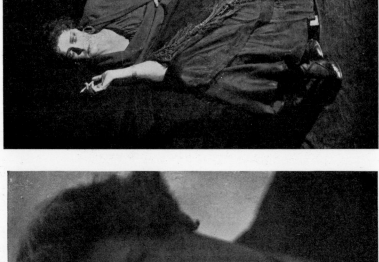

As the Spanish Gypsy
In "Carmencita and the Soldier"

In Life

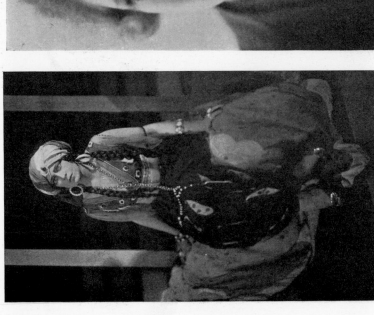

As Zarema
In "The Fountain of Bakhchi-Saraï"

OLGA BAKLANOVA, "WORTHY ARTIST OF THE REPUBLIC"

As Ange Pitou
In "The Daughter of Madame Angot"

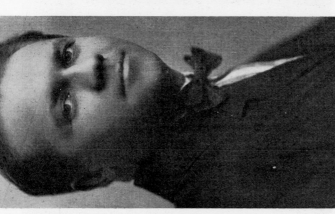

In Life

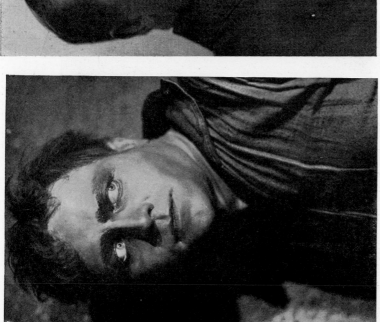

As José
In "Carmencita and the Soldier"

IVAN VELIKANOFF, TRAGEDIAN AND COMEDIAN

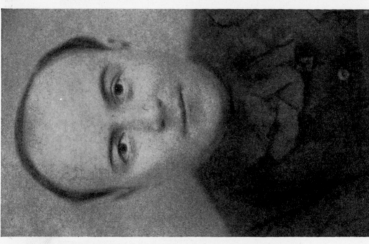

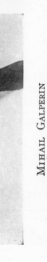

Mihail Galperin
Adapter of "The Daughter of Madame Angot" and "La Périchole"

Dmitry Smolin
Translator and Adapter of Aristophanes' "Lysistrata"

Constantin Lipskeroff
Poet and Author of "Carmencita and the Soldier"

THE DRAMATIC AUTHORS OF THE MUSICAL STUDIO

acting, do not pretend to be the vocal peers of the great grand opera companies. They have no thousand-dollar-a-night voices. But they can sing; they can act; and, what is more important, they can do both at the same time!

CHAPTER VI

REVOLUTIONS—FRENCH AND RUSSIAN

LECOCQ'S "THE DAUGHTER OF MADAME ANGOT"

WHEN Nemirovitch-Dantchenko set his hand to the renovation of the stagnant lyric stage, with the Synthetic Theatre
as his ultimate goal, he was in very much the same position
as Sergei Diagileff in the early days of the modern Russian
Ballet. He had a clear-cut conception of what he wished
to accomplish but, like Diagileff, he faced a field all but
barren of works written to be interpreted according to his
theories. The case of the Musical Studio, therefore, was
the reverse of that of the Moscow Art Theatre, for Tchehoff's plays existed as accomplished facts—hidden treasures
waiting for the divining rod of Stanislavsky and Nemirovitch-Dantchenko. That they even assisted these two young
regisseurs to crystallize their revolutionary theories of play
production is a plausible legend.

Probably the normal genesis of an esthetic theory is experiment, driven and directed by instinct, by an inner urge.
The theory in such a case arrives later, after the artist or
his critics have had an opportunity to judge and define the
significance of his work. Wagner is a case in point. Not
only his earlier works but the idea of the "Ring" came to
him out of the deep well of his unconscious imagination.
That he halted work on the latter to devote years of arduous

[62]

labor to the theoretical expression of his impelling idea in order that he might be full master of all his resources for the completion of his dream, does not alter the essential sequence of the processes. There are other minds, however, which foresee and understand the path ahead before ever setting foot on it. Still others, like Nemirovitch-Dantchenko, have been favored with facilities to follow either course according to the circumstances.

Since the new career and theory on which he was embarking offered to Nemirovitch-Dantchenko no lyric Tchehoffs waiting to exemplify that theory and to be stirred to life by it, the regisseur was compelled to seek among works embodying other theories those which were amenable to his own, and, preferably, those which could be improved thereby and developed into broader and deeper significance. This program, of course, would endure until improvised examples should stimulate creative artists to provide new material for express interpretation by the theory. If Nemirovitch-Dantchenko needed encouragement and assurance that his course would bear the desired fruit, he had only to recall Diagileff and the Ballet. In lieu of brief, intense, dramatic, choreographic themes and scores, that impressario reverted to Schumann for "Le Carnaval," to Chopin for "Les Sylphides," to Debussy for "L'Après-Midi D'un Faune," and to Rimsky-Korsakoff for "Shéhérazade." In doing so, he braved the wrath of musical purists, but in addition he not only achieved new intrinsic beauty, but also lit the fire that flamed into Stravinsky. Nemirovitch-Dantchenko's Stravinsky is still over the horizon, but the founder of the Musical Studio has already achieved rare and lasting beauty by his reinterpretation of classic plays and operas as lyric drama, as the Synthetic Theatre in embryo. Time, he is confident, will evolve the librettist and the composer of the Synthetic Theatre.

The regisseur faced a difficult problem in choosing the foundation stone of his repertory. His company consisted of young people, talented dramatically and vocally, but without experience. His theatre was a Studio, a workshop. That he still calls it a Studio today, after his novices have become expert and the daring bearers of a new dispensation across the lyric world, is testimony to the exalted ideals he cherishes. After all, life is a Studio, and he who calls his work finished is either complacent or presumptuous. For these novices, the first production had to be vocally simple. It did not matter how difficult were the technical problems facing the regisseur. With his experience, he could master them.

The choice, therefore, fell upon "The Daughter of Madame Angot," perhaps the best reason why the name of Charles Lecocq is a household word around the globe. As the Russian critic, Abram Efros, points out, its action is one of the classic examples of stage intrigue: "Two heroines love the same hero, and the hero courts the two at once. An accident reveals the truth, and the entire combination dissolves. The hero goes his way; one of the heroines, a wiser lady, returns to her former fiancé; the other reverts after her adventure to a rich and doting old lover." Stated thus baldly, the plot seems commonplace enough. But there must have been something, even before the innovations of the Russians, to endear it to thousands of audiences in France and England and all Europe as well as in America. That something consisted not only in Lecocq's ingenious and melodious score, but in a gallery of human and amusing character portraits etched by the original librettists, Clairville, Paul Siraudin and Victor Koning. Able hands, these, for Louis François Nicolaie, under the pseudonym Clairville, collaborated on "The Mysterious Stranger" and "The Chimes of Normandy," while Siraudin had a hand in "Le Courrier de Lyon," with which, as "The Lyons Mail," Sir Henry Irving curdled countless hearts.

"I selected 'The Daughter of Madame Angot,'" said Nemirovitch-Dantchenko to an interviewer during the rehearsals of the production in the spring of 1920, "first of all because it is a musical work of the highest order and in the second place because the subject of this work above all lent itself to our producing demands. Performers likewise were easier to select expressly for this piece. . . .

"A great many changes have been made, particularly in the musical relationships. For the sake of an integral, logically-connected impression, we made changes in the tempos, in the pauses, in the retards, etc. Most of my work was concerned with the individual performers in sketching out their portrayals, in adaptation and explanation, while a very great deal was prompted by the style of the music itself, which, of course, must blend with the mise en scène. It is interesting to note that music helps to make immense psychological leaps. Only with music and thanks to music, it does not seem incredible that Ange Pitou makes love to Lange ten minutes after he has met her!"

On the libretto, too, the regisseur laid his reshaping hand.

He summoned the poet, Mihail Galperin, to collaborate with him on the task of translation and revision. Galperin is a Little Russian. His father, a Kieff watchmaker, was too poor to send him to school, and the boy grew up alone over his books behind a board partition in the paternal shop where the only sound was the concerted chorus of clocks, large and small. Even to this day, he confesses, he does his best work to the ticking of numerous clocks which he has accumulated in his apartment with a collector's affection.

In the literary adaptation of "The Daughter of Madame Angot," the poet cites these two tasks he had to face: "to escape as far as possible, in the first place, from the traditional operetta genre and to shape the play as a lyrical musical-comedy, abounding in tenderly affecting as well as tragi-comic and simply comic situations; and in the second place to construct a scale of moods, building the whole libretto architecturally on the principles of harmonic progression and of effective and at the same time logical finale —the finale of each individual act as well as of the play as a whole. This latter general dénouement is a symbolical apologia for Poetry, free and unfettered by earthly laws. Ange Pitou's departure for new horizons and new conquests derives precisely and logically from the preceding clashes."

Surveying, then, the product of Galperin's remolding pen alongside the French original, we find dialog that is more natural and at the same time more rhythmic. In other words, the characters speak more plausibly in character without exchanging a certain necessary formality for a disillusioning realism. The sing-song formalism of light operatic routine has yielded to a light and vibrant artificiality.

In particular, the character of Ange Pitou, the ballad-monger and breaker of hearts, has been developed from a rather common, pasteboard figure of theatrical intrigue into a fascinating and sympathetic playboy. By deft and subtle touches, not by any wholesale interpolations, this picturesque product and pawn of revolution's wayward ways assumes the warmly human and three-dimensional aspect to which he has a right as an actual participant in the historic scenes of France's upheaval. The same process is apparent, too,

in the reworking of the other characters, notably those of the actress Lange, another figure borrowed directly from history, and the quaint, garrulous Mrs. Malaprop of the Markets, Amarante. Galperin and Nemirovitch-Dantchenko, apparently, have hit upon the happy idea of making this crusty old fish-wife the reincarnation of Clairette Angot's notorious mother and the repository of all the shrewd, resourceful traits which French legend and a score of plays have attributed to Madame Angot as archetype of the amusingly vulgar adventurer tossed up to sudden fame by the caprices of revolution.

Here and there, too, expanded or even inserted incident helps the narrative to flow more plausibly. A group of

wholly new characters from the Boulevards is pressed
into service just long enough to motivate the demand for
Pitou's latest barbed ballad in the first act. The plans for
the conspiracy in the second act are likewise roused out
of rut and routine.

But the one stroke which, more than any other, gives the
breath of new life to this classic of the lighter lyric stage,
is the finale of the last act. Of old, Pitou, spurned by the
undeceived daughter of Madame Angot, consoles himself
with Lange. In the Russian version, he who is spurned
spurns. His deceptions unmasked, this playboy poet wastes
no tears, seeks no surcease in false sentiment. From his
nimble tongue and undimmed spirit, then, come these lines,
translated by George S. and Gilbert Seldes from Galperin's
Russian text:

> "All of history records
> Lovers' quarrels end in peace,
> But it never works for me!
> A plague on this perfidious world,
> Farewell to all my enemies!

And a moment later, a refrain that returns from the
distance as the curtain falls:

> I've a poet's restless spirit,
> Roaming round for love and beauty.
> If these fail me, never mind,
> I'm content with mirth and laughter.

Into this reinvigorated score and libretto, the young
singing actors of the Studio, headed by the intense Baklanova in the rôle of Lange, plunged with such a will that

[68]

A GROUP OF FRENCH PEASANTS IN THE MARKET
A Scene from Act One

AN EPISODE IN THE FIRST ACT
(Left to right) Ivan Velikanoff as Ange Pitou, Nadiezhda Kemarskaya as Clairette
Angot, Dmitry Kamernitsky as Louchard and Vladimir Lossky as Larivaudière

"THE DAUGHTER OF MADAME ANGOT"

A GROUP FROM ACT TWO

(Left to right, seated) Nadiezhda Kemarskaya as Clairette, Vladimir Lossky as
Larivaudière, Olga Baklanova as Lange. (Standing) Dmitry Kamernitsky
as Louchard and Ivan Velikanoff as Ange Pitou

THE FIGHT IN ACT THREE BETWEEN CLAIRETTE AND LANGE

"THE DAUGHTER OF MADAME ANGOT"

they were ready for the premiere on May 16, 1920. The regisseur, too, had been busy with his rôle and by the aid of the artist, Maria Gortinskaya, he had hit upon an unrealistic and stylized expedient whereby the age of the French Directory could live convincingly once more and at the same time appear in quaint perspective. That expedient consisted in conceiving the play as an old French colored print come to life. As the curtain rises, the scenic setting and the inert figures on the stage are so lit as to convey the impression of an engraving, with its outlines sharply etched in a spirit of subdued caricature and with bright spots of color standing out against a slightly tinted background. It is two-dimensional, without perspective except the perspective of free-hand drawing. Slowly, then, as the light rises, the print comes to life. The characters, still preserving something of the spirit of caricature, act out and sing their compact, human and amusing little story, only to settle back and fade out once more at the finale into the quaint semblance of an old print.

In the light of the strides toward revolutionary and constructivist settings which Nemirovitch-Dantchenko and his scenic artists have made in the Musical Studio's later productions, the innovations introduced in "The Daughter of Madame Angot" seem timid and cautious, no matter how sound, appropriate and satisfying they may be on their own merits. As Efros says: "Time and experiment were necessary to arrive at the later scenic achievements. When we are told that the Musical Studio is only five years old, we must correct our natural impression by applying the great coefficient of revolution. Under revolution, five years be-

come an epoch, just as the period of 1789-93 did in France.
The solutions of 'The Daughter of Madame Angot' were
still simple and safe. But they had the double significance
of first experiments : No sooner did they discover what they
should avoid than they found their true aim. . . . In 1920
we thought that we were achieving the atmosphere and the
stylized formula of the Directory, and not a realistic and

documentary reproduction. As I look back on these dim
and beautiful pictures, however, I realize today that we had
not departed radically from the realistic settings which Dobu-
zhinsky, Benois, Roerich, Kustodieff and their fellows of
'The World of Art' had made for the Moscow Art Theatre
—a style which we thought we had put behind us.''

Nevertheless, the Musical Studio had moved scenically
far enough ahead of its parent that Alexander Benois
remarked on leaving the theatre after the performance of

"The Daughter of Madame Angot": "Evidently you wish to do away with the artist!"

Wholly apart from the technical problems of reorchestration, literary adaptation and reinterpretive scenic design, "The Daughter of Madame Angot," as the Russians give it, provides an evening of unmixed charm, a subtle blending of a smile, a chuckle and a sigh for the dear, dead past. Probably it wasn't any dearer or more amusing when Barras lived and ruled than our present will be when it becomes past, but distance makes it seem so. Distance and the expert hand of the regisseur who knows how to enhance the fascinations of distance!

Not only have Nemirovitch-Dantchenko's deft senses re-created the days of the Directory but they have brought trooping from the past the cherished memories of theatregoers whose recollections date back to the first performance of Lecocq's masterpiece over a half century ago. If it were to be revived today just as it was produced in Brussels in 1872, or in Paris, London and New York the following year, those memories probably would be sadly violated. Keeping in mind the developments in stagecraft of the last half century, who can honestly say he would like to see again the storied Marie Aimée as she sang the rôle of Clairette Angot at Daly's Broadway Theatre on August 25, 1873; Paola Marié or Mme. Théo in Maurice Grau's French company, Camille D'Arville at the Casino and Lillian Russell at the Garden, or even Mme. Alda at the New (now the Century) Theatre in December, 1909. All these and many others, however, will ride secure in the overtones of memory and tradition whenever the Russians sing.

[71]

It is not incredible that other than purely esthetic reasons may have guided Nemirovitch-Dantchenko in his choice of "The Daughter of Madame Angot" for his Musical Studio's coming-out costume. The political implications of the libretto by Clairville, Siraudin and Koning, sharply pointed by Lecocq's fluid and expressive score, have a heightened significance today, not only in the land of the most thoroughgoing revolution since the French, but also in a world through which that upheaval has reverberated. Just as someone has pointed out that "The Daughter of Madame Angot," satirizing ostensibly the French Directory of 1797, was really a veiled commentary on the French Government of the early '70's, when it was written, so its revival today may be taken by those who care to do so as a sly dig at the way the war has left intact the same personalities and the same shady customs and practices of prewar days. I may be mistaken, but it seemed to me that a thrill of recognition, a sense of contemporaneity, ran through the audience in Moscow during Ange Pitou's saucy verses at the end of the first act. I quote them here in the Seldes translation of Galperin's happy adaptation of the original French, for the sake of those who may care to surmise the plausibility of my impression:

> It's time for us to speculate
> How things are going with the State.
> Finance, as usual, is rotten;
> Hunger stares us in the face.
> But Lange, Larivaudière, Barras,
> Live on the fat of our dear land.

Oh, who can reach the heights above
To call the rascals to account?
And so this thing goes on forever,
It always was, and always will be.
And Lange, Larivaudière, Barras,
Will soon be crowned our kings and queens.

Forgotten are the people's woes
And France reduced to low estate.
The courtesans rule everywhere
And bring misfortunes in their wake.
Our boast of freedom is a sham,
The money-changers hold the throne,
The people are betrayed and fleeced,
By these new-crownèd kings and queens,
And so this thing goes on forever,
It always was, and always will be,
And Lange, Larivaudière, Barras,
Will soon be crowned our kings and queens.

We all were promised we'd be rich,
But Lange alone receives her share.
Graft is rampant as before
Among the petty bureaucrats.
We each may worry the other sick,
But all the profiteers are happy . . .
We have to live from hand to mouth
To gorge our friend, Larivaudière.
And so this thing goes on for ever,
It always was, and always will be.
And Lange, Larivaudière, Barras,
Will soon be crowned our kings and queens.

[73]

Other lines in Galperin's adaptation that strike home in Moscow and that lose none of their tang seven thousand miles away are:

"In republican times the only cheap light is sunlight."

"She imagined that under a Republic she could tell the truth."

"Since liberty reigns supreme in our country, I travel freely from prison to prison."

A barbed sidelight on Russia—under Tsar as well as Soviet—is tucked away in the middle of the second act when Clairette's unhappy fiancé, Pomponnet, is summarily arrested on the flimsiest circumstantial evidence.

How, you may ask, has it been possible for Nemirovitch-Dantchenko to give 262 performances in Moscow of a piece that flirts thus boldly with *lèse majesté* to the Soviet Régime? Of course, the Soviet can disown the allegation. But it may not even care to. Only those governments which are extremely young and fearful or senile and panicky make the mistake of choking the street-corner orator and the political satirist. Toleration means letting off steam; choking means driving the unrest under the surface where it can't be watched. The Soviet was once young and fearful and in that nervous mood it sacrificed and drove into exile the irrepressible Nikita Balieff. But saner councils got the upper hand with the melting away of the White armies, and by 1920 it was possible not only for Nemirovitch-Dantchenko to produce Lecocq's travesty on revolutionary government, but for Russian journalists and critics to comment frankly on its implications.

For nearly a decade now, a favorite parlor game in the

western world has been the drawing of parallels between the French and Russian Revolutions. No more picturesque or romantic comparison can be found than "The Daughter of Madame Angot" provides in its true-story poet hero, Ange Pitou. Across the checkerboard of successive régimes, history tells us that Pitou paraded the public squares of Paris with the product of his pungent pen, reposing his allegiance with a poet's whim where he pleased—now with Royalist, now with Republican. Locked up, released, subsidized, penalized, he was seldom put out of the way for long.

Ever since the early nervous days of the Russian Revolution, the populace of Moscow has been entertained by the practical jokes and political satires of the circus clowns, Bim and Bom, just as Ange Pitou beguiled the Parisian mob. Latterly their star has waned, after intermittent visits to various prisons for their temerity, but their place in the affections of the people has been taken by an even more daring satirist of the Government by the name of Bulganoff, whose mocking tales have a wider sale than any contemporary Russian writer. According to Walter Duranty of *The New York Times,* Bulganoff has recently been attacked in a ponderous editorial by *Izvestia,* the leading Government newspaper, which assails his "deplorable levity," "malicious lack of understanding," "fantastic astigmatism," and finally, "unfriendly bourgeois criticism, naked and unashamed." Bulganoff's sales immediately jumped. Rumor has it that even Trotsky himself enjoys his secret chuckle at Bulganoff's proscribed wit. And, while it isn't a matter of record, it isn't beyond belief that the theatre has proved once more its essentially contemporaneous nature by providing Bulganoff in "The Daughter of Madame Angot" with the incentive and example of his French prototype.

AS DESIGNER DREAMS AND REGISSEUR REALIZES

The First Act Setting for Lecocq's "The Daughter of Madame Angot." Above, the Sketch, in the Manner of an Old French Colored Print, by Maria Gortinskaya. Below, the Stage as Actually Disclosed on the Rise of the Curtain.

THE POMP AND POSTURE OF SPAIN IN THE VICEROY'S COURT AT LIMA
A Scene from Act Two

THE PRIMITIVE PASSIONS OF THE NATIVE PERUVIANS
Olga Baklanova as Le Périchole and Ivan Yagodkin as Piquillo in Act One
THE SHARP CONTRASTS OF OFFENBACH'S "LA PÉRICHOLE"

CHAPTER VII

OFFENBACH'S GAY MELODRAMA-BOUFFE

"LA PÉRICHOLE"

EMBOLDENED by the success of "The Daughter of Madame Angot" in particular and by the favorable reception of his project as a whole, Nemirovitch-Dantchenko determined to take a step in advance with his second production. But it must not be too difficult a step. He did not wish to overtax the dramatic talents of his young players by plunging them into tragedy nor their vocal equipment by saddling them with the responsibilities of true opera. They had proved themselves equal to opéra-comique; let them try once more in that genre, only with a piece of richer dramatic and vocal opportunities and sterner exactions. The choice fell naturally on Offenbach and on one of his less known but most characteristic compositions, "La Périchole."

Of this gay and exciting romance of Peru under the Spanish occupation, the poet Galperin, retained once more as translator and adapter, has written: "The exotic atmosphere, the ethnographic vividness of the locale and of the developments of the plot, the hot and sunny traits of a land of naïve feeling and divine sensuality—these are the causes and the secrets of the charms of this piece." And, it may be added, the causes and the secrets of the regisseur's choice of it. Few extant works of the lighter lyric stage give the sensitive and susceptible producer so ardent a hand-shake, few are so responsive to a reinvigorating imagination.

Furthermore, the history of "La Périchole" affords ample warrant for applying the hand of the reinterpreter. Performed for the first time in Paris on the stage of the Théâtre des Variétés, October 6, 1868, at the height of Offenbach's romantic career as composer, with the famous Hortense Schneider in the title rôle, "La Périchole" consisted of two acts—the first in the Plaza of Lima and the second at the court of the Viceroy. France and Russia were closely linked in spirit in those days, and this first version of the piece was soon translated by Victor Kruiloff for production at the Small State Theatre in Moscow and at the Alexandrinsky Theatre in Petersburg under the title of "Singing Birds." For its revival in Paris, six years after the premiere, Offenbach arranged with his librettists, Henri Meilhac and Ludovic Halévy, for a third act in two scenes—one in prison and the other in the Plaza. For continuing presentation in Russia, Kruiloff adopted the same and a few additional changes.

It is interesting to note in passing that the sleepless and ruthless will of the censor lay heavily on these early Russian productions. Don Andreas, Count of Ribiera, Viceroy of Peru, is the butt of the authors' most scathing satire. His absurd pretensions, inordinate pride and empty head are major elements in all of the comic situations. Now, viceroyalty is next door to royalty, and, as such, must be protected from mockery's minions. To save the face of regal power, therefore, we have the paradoxical spectacle of the

"LA PÉRICHOLE"
Costume Sketches by Pierre Konitchalovsky

Tsar's agents deposing the Viceroy in Offenbach's opéra-comique and making him a Governor; while in the Russian provinces, where even the rôle of Governor had to be swathed in irreproachable dignity, Don Andreas had to be content with a Vice-Governorship! The other and more diverting side of the paradox, of course, emerges when the Soviet, hater of monarchy, permits Nemirovitch-Dantchenko to restore the demoted official to kingly rank, just because Offenbach makes him the victim of ridicule!

Almost everywhere "La Périchole" was sung, it had the record of being done in both the original and revised version. The former was used, of course, at its American premiere, January 4, 1869, at Pike's Opera House, later the Grand Opera House, where it had the honor of falling just within the first year of the checkered career of that would-be rival of the Academy of Music. The short version, too, was the one which Briot gave at the Fourteenth Street Theatre soon after. Probably both versions appeared during the decade of Maurice Grau's French company, while Paola Marié in the early '80's and Lillian Russell at the Knickerbocker in April, 1895, undoubtedly used the extended form. There is no record of any third version or of drastic revisions for American production and, of course, no meddling of a censor.

Even though the regisseur may not be conscious of it, I suspect that the artist's natural instinct against tampering with the completed work of another artist has been weakened in the case of Nemirovitch-Dantchenko and all Russian producers by the frequency with which the censor has hacked and hashed the manuscripts of playwrights, native and foreign. The utterly inviolate manuscript, literary or dramatic, is almost unknown in Russia. Nevertheless, as I have shown, Offenbach himself set the Musical Studio an

example in revision. Stimulated by this example, by his firm conviction that the librettists of the nineteenth century were inferior to their composers, and by the auspicious outcome of his first venture, Nemirovitch-Dantchenko applied the reshaping process more radically to both the literary and musical material of "La Périchole" than he had done to that of "The Daughter of Madame Angot." In keeping with this bolder policy, too, he extended his scenic outposts in this production farther toward the "left wing" of modern art.

The manifest comparisons and contrasts with "The Daughter of Madame Angot" were further warrant for this course. Like "Angot," "La Périchole" beneath its romantic exterior is a social and political satire. On the other hand, this ironic note is less dominant. "The Daughter of Madame Angot" is satire depicted against a background of romance and fantasy. "La Périchole" is a fullblooded and fantastic romance depicted against a background of satire. History in Offenbach's work plays a lesser rôle. The hand of the regisseur of "La Périchole," therefore, is freer to experiment with character and situation for the sake of a heightened dramatic effect.

Taking his cue from the dual spirit that is obvious in the score and latent in the libretto, Nemirovitch-Dantchenko stressed and heightened the exuberant moments, emphasized and deepened the pathetic episodes, achieving unsuspected effects by the sharp alternation of these intensified moods. Simultaneously, in similar manner and with like effect, he brought to focus and played off against one another the intimately lyrical scenes and those of grotesque humor. In brief, what was once an opéra-comique has become in Russian hands a melodrama-bouffe.

The most radical alteration and the one which, at a stroke, accomplished most of his desired ends is the metamorphosis of Périchole and Piquillo from Spaniards into native Peruvians and, what is more to the point, from a pair of rather sophisticated street singers, whose relationship may be taken for granted, into two naïve youths, almost children. By this change, Nemirovitch-Dantchenko has not only made the story more plausible but far more poignant. Their lamentation in the first act over the fact that they can not kiss because they haven't money enough to buy a marriage license, paves the way for a scene of great lyric power and passionate intensity when, after their strange marriage to suit the personal whims of the  Viceroy, they stretch their chains taut in their prison cell to press lip against lip. Furthermore, the character of Périchole herself becomes far more significant, more rewarding to the interpreting singer-actress and to the listening spectator. As the action unfolds in the Russian version, this half-child, half-untamed-animal of the first act grows into a mature woman, compelled to use all her suddenly awakened instincts, intuitions and intelligence to maintain her independence. Probably the French audiences of the mid-nineteenth century didn't give a fig for psychological truth in opéra-comique, but Nemirovitch-Dantchenko has shrewdly anticipated the demands of his public today by stressing the rapidity with which a young girl comes into her own and by showing how it is Périchole's awakened faculties that come to the rescue of the dull-witted Piquillo. This reanimated, varicolored and impassioned Périchole, of course, is easily within the range of Baklanova's sensitive and intense genius for characterization, and her little Peruvian street singer, who defies the Viceroy's wiles and temptations to be true to her humble lover, is a portrait strikingly contrasted with her sophisticated and caustic Lange in "The Daughter of Madame Angot."

Once more, in the scenes where the Spanish forces of occupation confront the native Peruvians, Nemirovitch-Dantchenko has deepened his appeal to contemporary thought and feelings by filling in with illuminating detail the fear, suspicion, pride and overbearing of the conquerors on the one hand and the inner hatred, the outward submission, the alertness, the shrewdness and the resourcefulness of the conquered on the other hand. Armies of occupation meant little to the world of 1868. But to the world of 1925, still smarting from the arbitrary sanctions of the Ruhr and still remembering how the World War was urged on if not directly caused by the abuse of the conquered by the conqueror, a simple, artificial formula is insufficient. Choruses calling each other naughty names satisfied Offenbach, his librettists and his audiences. For us today, Nemirovitch-Dantchenko has had the wisdom to provide genuine illusion by means of subtle shading and innuendo and by the creation of an atmosphere of ominous suspense. To this end he has more sharply individualized the several high Spanish dignitaries, giving Semyon Rakhmanoff, for instance, a rich opportunity as the sycophantic Count Panatellas and Leonid Baratoff full leash for his grotesque comic powers as the pompous Don Pedro; while as spokeswomen for the native side he has transformed the buxom keepers of the Three Sisters' Tavern from Spaniards and pasteboard figures into Peruvians and major participants in the intrigue.

One of the happiest alterations in the Russian libretto is the result of accident. For the premiere of "La Périchole" on July 14, 1922, the regisseur cast Vassily Luzhsky, of the Art Theatre's Dramatic Company, as the Viceroy. Now Luzhsky, who stands in the first line of the theatre's acting ranks and who is vividly remembered in America for his Bubnoff in "The Lower Depths," his Firce in "The Cherry Orchard," his Shouisky in "Tsar Fyodor" and his Fyodor Pavlovitch in "The Brothers Karamazoff," was not blessed by God with a professional singing voice, although, like all Russians, he can sing. In his own person, the Viceroy has no great vocal responsibilities, but in the prison scene of the third act he appears disguised as the Jailer and sings the celebrated number, "The Merry Keys." For Luzhsky's

[83]

sake, therefore, it was deemed discreet to turn the rôle of the Jailer into a dumb part.   The song of the keys, accord-

ingly, emerges as pantomime, but such illuminating panto- mime as only the Moscow Art Theatre can provide. The success of this innova- tion was so startling that it was retained even after Vladimir Lossky, of the Mu- sical Studio's regular roster, had replaced Luzhsky in the rôle of the viceroy.

So thoroughgoing a revision of the libretto, of course, suggests that this process may have its echo in the score of the Russian production.   It has, and a much sharper echo than in "Angot."   To keep in step with the new form and spirit of plot and characterization in "La Périchole," the Studio's conductor, Vladimir Bakaleynikoff, has cut Offen- bach's music here, expanded it there, and has changed sev- eral of the individual numbers in sequence and even in application and orchestration.   Among the most important departures from the composer's own last revisions, the fol- lowing deserve mention: An authentic Spanish song has been inserted in the first act for Piquillo and his guitar, while the finale of the same act has been supplemented by a few dozen bars expressive of the smoldering resentment of the Peruvians over the Spanish order to substitute circus antics for native rites and customs in Périchole's wedding ceremony.

OFFENBACH'S "LA PÉRICHOLE"

The Setting for Act One, the Plaza in Front of the Inn of the Three Sisters, as Designed by Pierre Kontchalovsky

THE SINGING BIRDS IN PRISON

(Kneeling) Boris Belostotsky as Piquillo and Olga-Baklanova as
La Périchole

THE CONSPIRATORS

(Left to right) Semyon Rakhmanoff as Count Panatellas, Vladimir Lossky as the Viceroy, and Leonid Baratoff as Don Pedro

BUFFOONERY ALTERNATES WITH LYRIC INTENSITY IN OFFENBACH'S "LA PERICHOLE"

In the second act, the musically brilliant trio, "The Ladies," is divorced from its commonplace words and its rather banal setting in the hands of the Viceroy, Piquillo and Don Pedro and moved forward to the opening of the act where the French Court-Lady, to the accompaniment of a chorus of Spanish ladies-in-waiting, turns it into a pert and subtle tribute to the power of women over men, while Spanish fans, adroitly handled in the language of Castile, serve as eloquent aids to words and music.

The prison scene of the third act has a new musical finale incidental to the locking of the discomfited Viceroy in the cell—the distant and disconnected intrusions of a bolero from a nuptial festival, without bridegroom, without bride, without god-father; warning shots (what sort of a melodrama is it that has no gun-fire?);

and the sad ruminations of a Viceroy who has been cast to the dogs, conveyed, to the accompaniment of an ominous tremolo of the violins played *sul ponticello*, by a solo on the French horn repeating the theme of "It is sad when jealous pangs . . ." with which his Majesty had just a moment before twitted his two prisoners.

Between the first and second scenes of the third act, Bakaleynikoff has inserted an intermezzo in the style of Offenbach. The score of the last scene, in turn, is considerably altered throughout in accordance with the note of popular unrest culminating in open rebellion which has been interpolated in the Russian libretto. And the duet of Périchole and Piquillo, "Singing Birds," the touching lament of two lovers, is scarcely recognizable, through the changed harmony, orchestration and motion, as the care-free third figure of Offenbach's quadrille.

If the hand of the fearless innovator is boldly apparent in the libretto and the score of "La Périchole," à la Russe, its presence is felt with equally striking results in the scenic settings and the costumes. Nemirovitch-Dantchenko extended his outposts simultaneously in all directions, and in line with this policy he chose Pierre Kontchalovsky to design his second production. If any proof were needed that the regisseur of the Musical Studio was moving away from the realism of the Moscow Art Theatre as rapidly as his own expanding imagination, the tastes of his public and the maturing talents of his collaborating artists would permit, this choice must have settled the argument.

For over twenty years, Kontchalovsky himself had been moving farther and farther toward the "left wing" of modern art. Matriculating at the Academy Julian, he fled from the Quartier Latin and the classes of Jean-Paul Laurens and Benjamin Constant, to Brittany, the ocean and freedom. A little later, about 1900, he deserted the Academy of Fine Arts in Petersburg in like manner to live and paint with the fishermen of Archangel on the shores of the White Sea. Italy—the Umbrian countryside, rather than the Roman galleries; the Siberian Tatars; Paris again; Madrid, and intermittent homecomings—these wanderings gave sustenance to his imagination and his brush until the

[86]

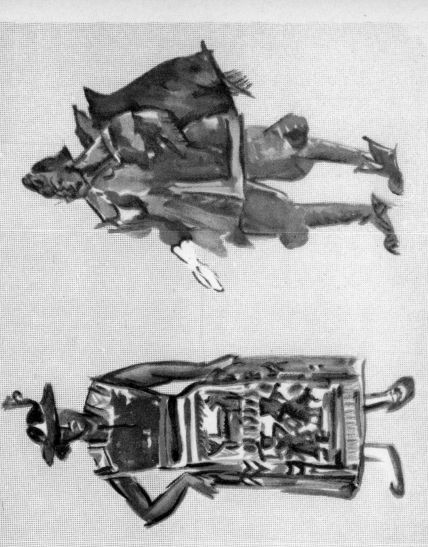

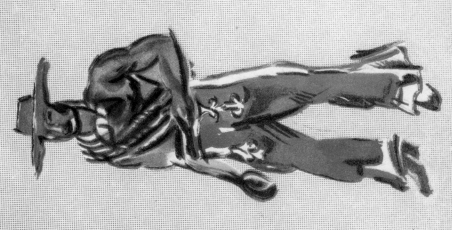

"LA PÉRICHOLE"

Costume Sketches by Pierre Konchalovsky

war mobilized him. Chief of the Russian cubists, one of the founders of the radical group, "Bubnovy Valyet," apologist at home for Cézanne, Derain, Picasso, Légere and Gleizes, he returned last season to western Europe, bringing with him none of the war's tragic obsessions which still oppress Occidental painters. Hailed every-where as the new link with eternal Russia, he won fresh laurels, representation in the collection of the Carnegie Institute, of Pittsburgh, and official recognition in his Paris catalog from de Monzie, French Minister of Public Instruction. His portrait in those pages is so vivid that I must quote it:

"Of the Slavs who have appeared in our pictural Occident, Kontchalovsky is the least morbid, the most incapable of neurosis. On large tranquil shoulders, a solid head, firmly attached; eyes without troubled light or uncertain frenzy but so clear and so laughing that one would call them cheerful; the carriage of a good clever giant for whom no effort is ever attended by pain, for whom all is vitality and health, for whom everything in his talent as well as in his character proceeds from a sincere joy of living and of working. Kontchalovsky paints in the same manner as the peasants work the plains of Russia.

When the peasant sows and when he ploughs the ground,
He sees only his seed, his oxen and his furrow.

"Pierre Kontchalovsky is very similar in his method and his drawing to the mystical farmer of Alfred de Musset. No reasoned-out system of esthetics, no theory of art!

"No picture-program, no landscape-lecture! Certainly not because he disdains to know the theories incessantly promulgated. He stops just long enough to take a drink on the terrace of a café, then goes on his free road with a rekindled enthusiasm. Sometimes in an important presence he is polite enough to appear to submit to another's influence; for he is a gentleman, even as regards fashion, that woman of the world, but his vocation is that of a rebel with good manners."

In that phrase, "a rebel with good manners," lies the secret of Kontchalovsky's contribution to the scenic annals of the Moscow Art Theatre Musical Studio. Conservative admirers of the Art Theatre's realistic traditions may stand aghast at the mere choice of this "atrocious schematist and deformer of nature, this bugbear of journalists and of well-bred people." In quieter times (if it is conceivable that the Musical Studio could have come into being at all under such conditions), that choice would have been revolutionary. Even in Moscow, 1922, it was a shock. On the other hand, connoisseurs from the "left wing" were equally disturbed at the sight of Kontchalovsky's finished work for "La Périchole." Where was their cubist, their bad boy of the arts? When he had an opportunity to make faces on the proper platform of the Art Theatre, why didn't he do it?

Both of these extreme camps can be answered in the same breath. Nemirovitch-Dantchenko, with that almost uncanny power of artistic intuition which all great regisseurs have,

[88]

detected in Kontchalovsky the "rebel with good manners."
For the logical development of his theatre he had to move
forward—to the "left," if you will. But he had to move
deliberately, step by step. And he preferred an artistic revolutionist who knew how to behave on necessary occasion, to
a conservative on a spree. The former has a better conception of the esthetic theories of revolt, and, no matter how
he keeps himself in hand, the effervescent spirit of revolt
bursts out from time to time to enliven the party. Justifying
Nemirovitch-Dantchenko's faith in him and in his tact,
Kontchalovsky approached his task, not in the spirit of an
easel painter who is going to reform the stage, but in that
of a theatrical craftsman who respects his medium and
determines to use it to its full capacity. He knew that he
had been selected, not for the purpose of honoring intransigence, but because he had the good grace to serve a growing
cause at a crucial moment and because, methods and theories aside, he knew as an artist "more about nature than
nature knows about herself," in the words of Efros.

To the setting for the first and fourth scenes of "La
Périchole," therefore, Kontchalovsky brought his love of
great dimensions, expressed through means peculiar to the
theatre. The expanse of out-of-doors is here, made hot and
vibrant by daring use of contrasting colors. The artist is
master of his stage space, too, in the court scene—the trans-
planted Spain which he had known during his student days
and which he suggests rather than details by the use of
leading motives of design and tone. The prison scene is
even more subtly convincing with its washed-out tones of
an underground dungeon. But it is in the costumes that

[89]

Kontchalovsky has let himself go oftener than in the settings. There is a mood of touch-and-go about them that makes them almost masks of the characters who wear them. He is especially successful in the cases of the absurd Spanish officials and of the Three Sisters. And if, as the verdict in Moscow stands today after "Lysistrata" and "Carmencita and the Soldier," Kontchalovsky's "La Périchole" joins Gortinskaya's "Angot" as another transitional step, as too much mere painting—new painting, but still painting—and too little dynamic stage architecture, the artist may have the satisfaction of knowing that his work served as stepping stones to an otherwise inaccessible rock midstream.

CHAPTER VIII

The Humors of the Immortal Greeks

ARISTOPHANES' "LYSISTRATA"

THE rock midstream, which had loomed but dimly from the bank and to which "Madame Angot" and "La Périchole" were stepping stones, proved to be that gay, hale and ageless bequest from the days of the immortal Greeks, Aristophanes' "Lysistrata." Seeking the fundamental principles of a living lyric drama and confident that he would find them in the process of daring experiment, Nemirovitch-Dantchenko was drawn to this unexpected choice for his third production by factors as logical as they were unpremeditated. Greek comedy a haven on the way to lyric drama, to a modern Synthetic Theatre? Nevertheless, Greek or Russian, antique or modern, comedy or tragedy, "Lysistrata" answered the regisseur's purpose. For his company of young singing actors, equal now to harder tasks than opéra-comique imposes, he needed a piece that would put them on their mettle dramatically, vocally and plastically.

Now, the Greek theatre made just these same coördinate demands on its participants. Unfortunately, most of the plays in the Greek tragic canon also demand in their audience a frame of mind that has passed forever from the earth—a naïve faith in heroic legends, an exalting acquiescence in sacrifice for ideals that seem futile to us; while few of the Greek comedies make vital contact with our contemporary social, political and moral issues. "Lysistrata" is a glowing exception. While answering the regisseur's technical requirements, this racy old record of feminine revolt in ancient Athens is just as alive, just as stimulating, today as it was when Aristophanes produced it in 411 B. C. at the gloomiest moment of the Peloponnesian War, braving the wrath of the public, playing the leading rôle himself when professional actors struck and molding a mask of yeast, according to tradition, when the mask-makers refused to have anything to do with the production. Amazing as it may be, the coin of its leading motives is still current after nearly two and a half millenniums—war, peace, nature, health, men, women, sexual desire. And the conflict between these motives is just as far from solution.

Perception of this vitality, this contemporary significance, in "Lysistrata" is the keynote of lines by Dmitry Smolin, author of the Russian version of the play, published in *Programs* a few weeks before the premiere on June 16, 1923. "Our age of supreme activity rather than meditation," says Smolin, "of creation rather than philosophy, is the age of farce and tragedy rather than of comedy and drama. Through Aristophanes it is possible to restore to the frivolous theatre its full weight, value, importance and vitality as well as its human and social function. That is why, aside from its purely theatrical effect, the production of 'Lysistrata' can have a great social and human significance."

With this sound, intelligent and realistic respect for Aristophanes, which the regisseur shared with Smolin, it

LYSISTRATA (LYDIA BELYAKOVA)
Startles the Women of Athens by Her Proposal of a Love Strike to Compel Peace

LYSISTRATA (YELIZAVETA GUNDOBINA)
Binds the Women by an Oath into a League

TWO EPISODES AND TWO LYSISTRATAS IN ARISTOPHANES' COMEDY

THE OLD MEN AND THE WOMEN OF ATHENS BIDDING FOR THE FAVOR OF THE
AUDIENCE

AT THE HEIGHT OF THE BATTLE BETWEEN THE OLD MEN AND THE WOMEN

ARISTOPHANES' "LYSISTRATA"
Two Scenes and Two Angles of Rabinovitch's Constructivist Setting

LYSISTRATA SURVEYS THE ROUT OF THE OLD MEN BY THE WOMEN

THE CELEBRATION OF THE PEACE

ARISTOPHANES' "LYSISTRATA"
Two More Scenes and Angles of Rabinovitch's Greece in Epitome

ARISTOPHANES' "LYSISTRATA"

Grotesque Episodes in the Battle between the Old Men of Athens and the Women,
Led by Lysistrata

was natural that their aim in the Russian version should be to preserve as faithfully as possible not only the spirit of the original but also its form. Never did it enter their heads to make of it an operetta-bouffe, as Adelardo Fernández-Arias and C. L. de Cuenca did for the Teatro de la Zarguela in Madrid in 1905, with music by Paul Lincke. Intellectual prostitution would probably be their verdict on the celebrated Maurice Donnay adaptation, with its decadent pandering to the boulevardier and its interpolated scene among the Athenian courtesans, which was produced at the Grand Théâtre in Paris in December, 1892, and which has had revivals in 1896, 1909, and latterly with revisions in 1919. Even the Laurence Housman adaptation, frank to the point of making the Lord Chamberlain think twice before licensing Gertrude Kingston's production at the Little Theatre, London, in October, 1911, and provocative of "oh's" and "ah's" at the performance under the auspices of the Women's Political Union at Maxine Elliott's Theatre the year before the war, would seem timid and evasive. And the accepted collegiate version of B. B. Rogers, with its convenient omission of all downright lines and situations, would be beneath their scorn. The full blood and vigor and tang of Aristophanes—gusty humor, grotesque by-play, intimate glimpses into masculine and feminine psychology, lyric beauty and exalted moral indignation— this was their goal, just as it has been the goal of George S. and Gilbert Seldes in their admirable English translation of Smolin's Russian text.

Courage, craftsmanship, a sense of humor and social vision—these were the qualities necessary to a living, breathing text of "Lysistrata." Rarely as they are discovered together, the requisite talents for reconstructing a musical score are still more elusive. Generally speaking, there are not more than fifteen minutes of ancient Greek music extant today. The problem of how and when the Greeks used music in their dramatic performances is one that has been argued to weariness and boredom by archæologists. After all, the test of an attempt to compose a score today in the alleged vein of Greek music should be: Does it enhance the mood of the text, does it add to the dynamics of the production? The verdict on the achievement of Reinhold Gliere in his score for "Lysistrata" must be an emphatic affirmative.

As the eminent Russian critic, A. Kugel, puts it in *Theatre and Music,* "there is not enough music in 'Lysistrata' to make you think it an opera, but there is enough to assure you that it is not a drama." A drama, that is, in the sense of the modern realistic theatre. In other words, Gliere has not written a continuous score. His music arises from the rational demands of the moment—now as definite lyric accompaniment to choral song, now as unobtrusive but colorful partner to the action. Its entrances and exits are not abrupt, for it makes its appearance as the extension of the pitched intonation of speech. The ancient Greek tone scales, notably the Phrygian and the Dorian, are utilized with a strange, other-worldly effect that is arresting and stimulating without seeming affected. "Lysistrata," therefore, will introduce a new aspect of the talent of a composer already known in this country, largely through two symphonic works, "Ilya Muromets," performed by the Chicago Symphony Orchestra, and "The Sirens," some chamber music and a few songs. Pupil of Taneyeff and Ippolitoff-Ivanoff at the Moscow Conservatory, Gliere has ranged through two creative periods, a symphonic and a vocal, and he is now in the midst of a dramatic period. The Musical Studio is bringing still another example of this latter talent in his "Cleopatra," a mimo-drama suggested by Pushkin's "Egyptian Nights."

If utter fidelity to the original text and an intuitional reconstruction of the musical background sufficed for these elements of the production, Nemirovitch-Dantchenko realized, before he had gone far with the physical side, that wholly new creative vision was necessary to recapture the visual spirit of Greek comedy and express it not only in terms comprehensible to the audience of today but by means of expedients available in the present-day theatre. A slavish effort to duplicate a performance of Arisophanes' era would be as artificial and strained and abnormal as the frequent attempts to copy an Elizabethan performance—an archæological holiday, no more, no less. Instead, both the grotesque and the lyric moments must be heightened in order that they may register on senses unaccustomed to their contrasting moods. Furthermore, the stage setting must become architectural and plastic, rather than pictorial and static. Only thus do the monumental proportions of the Greek theatre come to life. Only thus can the audience be swept up into a sense of participation with the players, of unconscious, self-denying, Dionysian ecstasy.

Various critics and producers have suspected that in the plastic forms of so-called modern art lay hidden the secret means of recapturing the spirit of this heroic theatre of the ancients as well as of realizing the straining ambitions of a contemporary heroic theatre. Heretofore, however, we have progressed little beyond the statement of the problem: How can the theatre of today utilize the astounding developments which the painter and the sculptor—the cubist, the futurist, the expressionist, the constructivist—have achieved in their respective fields?

Failure to solve this problem has not been due to lack of attempts. I do not take into consideration the broader quest of Gordon Craig and Adolph Appia to establish scenic design and the theatre as a whole once more on an artistic foundation, for that quest has borne rich fruit in every land. But the more explicit problem has been dotted with disaster and half-success—in America, the Jones-Hopkins "Macbeth," and the productions of certain plays of O'Neill, Glaspell, Lawson and Rice by our institutional theatres; in Germany, the motion picture, "The Cabinet of Dr. Caligari"; in Italy, the futurist experiments of Marinetti; in Russia itself, the productions of Meyerhold and the Kamerny Theatre. In some cases, the producer has strangled the scenic artist; in others, the latter has seized the reins and gone on an esthetic spree; in still others, fear of the public and compromise have been responsible.

What all these attempts lacked was a directing personality of profound imagination, of supreme tolerance and catholicity of taste, of vast experience and of firm will-power. Such a personality can command the respect and allegiance of the modern artist, if he in turn be equally tolerant and broad-minded, and can enlist him, not as an easel painter translating his conceptions into terms of the theatre, but as

[96]

a fellow-craftsman in the theatre dealing in space as well as in color and line—a painter-sculptor or a painter-architect, if you will. Then, by giving him to understand that *within the precincts of his craft* he need fear no restricting hand, the miracle is possible. Here, in terms so simple that seekers after startling secrets may be disappointed, is that golden mean between freedom and the leash which provides the greatest incentive to any creative artist. If the solution to the problem seems simple in theory, however, it is still difficult and distant in practice. In other words, you must find your directing personality of protean gifts.

Such a personality the Moscow Art Theatre Musical Studio possesses in Vladimir Nemirovitch-Dantchenko. As we have seen, though, even he approached the problem by degrees, coming face to face with it only in "Lysistrata." What it meant to him to come to terms with modern art, to employ one of its most brilliant representatives in Russia, Isaac Rabinovitch, and to give his genius unrestricted play, he confesses with his accustomed frankness in *Amusements:*

"In the production of 'Lysistrata' a whole series of the canons of the older producers was violated. When after forty years I stopped smoking—it was not easy. While producing 'Lysistrata' and working in contact with the designer Rabinovitch, it was not so easy for me to infringe upon my traditions as an old-line realist. It all started with the decision to have the characters make their entrance on the stage through a trap—a violation of the plausibility and the logic of the realistic theatre. Having permitted myself one liberty, I proceeded to permit a second and a third. To break is to break!"

"Lysistrata"—visually—certainly breaks with all the traditions of the realistic theatre. I say visually with reason, for it is not merely a question of stage scenery in the accepted and limited sense. The actual, tangible setting comprises merely a few columns, pediments, staircases and platforms—the sublimation of the Acropolis and the Parthenon in ivory white against a deep blue sky. The significant thing is the way this simple setting rules and molds the action, the way the action rules and molds the setting, the way they interact and react on each other with a precision and an economy of means that fill the eye without confusing it. Even so vast a production as "The Miracle" does not appeal more continuously to the visual sense. As presented on the Art Theatre's revolving stage, with the circular platform and the spare but exquisite symbol of all that once was Greece now at rest, now moving deliberately, now whirling madly and frantically, the visual embodiment of this pungent and rocketing old comedy is ever fresh, ever alive, ever stimulating.

Here is no mere trick, no sheer "stunt" in stage mechanism. That it is arresting, exciting, thrilling, goes without saying. Neither is this use of the revolving stage a mere convenience and time-saver in changing scenes, much less an adaptation of the Japanese and the Reinhardt fantasy of showing a player setting out for his destination, disclosing him en route, and finally bringing him to journey's end as the stage comes to rest. When this substantial structure first begins to turn on its axis, you have the disconcerting feeling of being uprooted from familar moorings, as if the very ground were shifting beneath your feet. As it comes

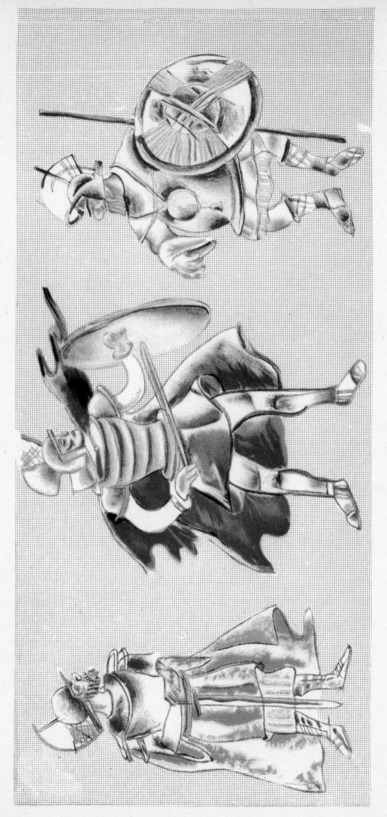

"LYSISTRATA"
Costume Sketches by Isaac Rabinovitch

to rest, your eye is rewarded with a new angle of beauty. Turning once more, and more rapidly, it serves to heighten the excitement of the grotesque conflict between the old men of Athens and the women of all Greece who have banded together under Lysistrata with a vow to "abstain from men" until their men make peace. And finally, as peace is signed, the leaping and jubilant procession of the populace in the opposite direction to that of the moving structure gives the startling impression of the Parthenon frieze come to life!

Even if the visual embodiment of "Lysistrata" fulfilled only these three superficial services—sensational dynamic accompaniment to the action, rapidity of scene changes, and visual continuity of the action—it would be a tour de force in stage craftsmanship. But it is something more—how much more, one is not likely to realize until second observation when, to the amazement of those who set it all down as a clever trick, the thrill is as sharp as it was with the edge of novelty still keen.

To analyze this deeper value, this lasting power to stimulate, would carry us far into the heart of one of the most venerable of the arts. For Moscow's "Lysistrata" is nothing more nor less than architecture. Rabinovitch's problem was the problem of handling space—not the primary and tractable dimensions of length and breadth plus a third dimension consisting of the illusion of perspective, a combination which usually serves the theatre's spacial and architectural demands. Space in the absolute sense was his raw material, for his pillared group had to be perfect from every point on its circumference, just like a great cathedral or a

Mogul's tomb round which men walk and stand and gaze at the varying vista. Constructivism is the term applied in Europe today to this effort to handle space absolutely rather than illusively. The trouble with most of the constructivists, in the first place, is that they have conceived their inspiration in machinery rather than in architecture, and in the second, that they have wrecked their machinery—and their space— in deference to specious social motives. Rabinovitch, how- ever, is on surer ground, for he not only respects the past but thereby has a finer respect for the present. As Frances Fineman has written in *The New York Times:* "Though making use of modern tendencies and influenced as all work- ers in the Russian theatre are by the stimulus of Meyerhold, Rabinovitch tends to cling to the conservative tradition. There is, moreover, a curiously American quality about his designing: it is clean-cut and decisive and economical."

One could roam far afield, too, in speculating metaphysic- ally on Rabinovitch's "Lysistrata." If, as he says, "This is Hellas!" literal-minded folk may justly ask, "Why, then, join your columns by curving pediments?" Of course, the literal-minded answer is that spectators in a theatre can not pick and choose their vantage ground for succeeding glimpses of the architectural mass. They must take it from their seats as it comes to them—in the round. And in the round it must be molded—ironically enough, a new convention, a new illusion, sprouting out of a technique that defies con- vention! But there is also an answer which philosophical students may prefer. Perhaps Rabinovitch is convinced with Einstein that all space is relative, that parallel lines meet at infinity and that the outer walls of the universe turn all

A Crucial Moment in the Battle between the Old Men and the Women of Athens

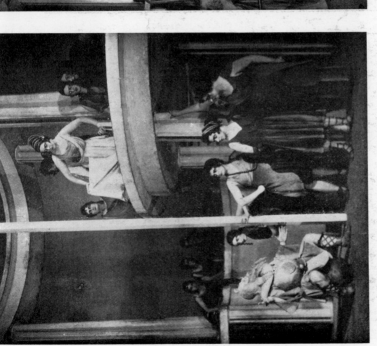

Probulos (Leonid Baratoff) Is Worsted in His Duel of Tongue-Lashing with Lysistrata (Olga Baklanova)

ARGUMENT AND ACTION IN ARISTOPHANES' "LYSISTRATA"

THE SEX STRIKE PUT TO THE TEST IN ARISTOPHANES' "LYSISTRATA"

straight lines back on themselves on a curve—in other words, that "Lysistrata" is not only Hellas in microcosmus but the universe viewed on the same scale!

The artist who has thus brought something new and endlessly disputatious into the theatre is barely thirty, a product of Kieff and the artistic circle mothered by Alexandra Exter, the celebrated designer of Wilde's "Salome" for the Kamerny Theatre. At an early age, he caught the fiery soul of the theatre as men "get religion," and for six or seven years he has tried his hand on many of Moscow's stages as well as in the motion pictures. Probably his most notable work aside from his "Lysistrata" and his "Carmencita and the Soldier" for Nemirovitch-Dantchenko is his setting for Goldfaden's "The Sorceress" at Granovsky's Jewish Kamerny Theatre. Despite his youth, Rabinovitch treads his path with mature assurance, guiding himself by the watchwords, Simplicity, Stability and Expediency. On the other hand, despite his assurance, the theatre is to him an endless adventure. Witness this characterization by Efros:

"Watch Rabinovitch when he is at work on the stage, parceling out the available space in three dimensions or when he is making a stage model. Here is a new race of stage designer. He has a strange receptivity, a different eye and unusual hands. He lives on the stage as if he were born on it. For him this is absolute atmosphere and absolute soil. Stanislavsky says: 'When an actor and a chance visitor walk side by side across the stage, their feet touch the floor differently: one merely walks on the boards, the other on "new ground." ' For Rabinovitch the stage is ever such 'new reality.' "

[101]

Although Nemirovitch-Dantchenko collaborated intimately with Rabinovitch in devising sharply expressive means of using the stage setting intensively, and although the actor-singer ensemble—the mob—is difficult to divorce from the setting, seeming to be merely the most dynamic and most plastic part of it, I can not pass on without a tribute to the regisseur's handling of that mob. In the words of the critic, P. Markoff, "the solution of the moods of the crowd was the solution of the performance." And from Dr. Sergei Berthensson we get this pen picture of "Lysistrata's" human panorama: "Strange and abrupt movements; brightly colored mass costumes, utterly at variance with traditional theatrical vestments; wholesome sunburned faces and bodies; wild outcries from the men, from the women; a mob, actual, living, disorderly; a galloping tempo."

I doubt whether any other aspect of the repertory of the Musical Studio marks more clearly the decisive break with the naturalistic traditions of the Art Theatre than the mob of "Lysistrata." Recall to mind, if you will, the heterogeneous crowd that gathered in Captain Horster's home in "An Enemy of the People" to hear Dr. Stockmann's speech— Knipper-Tchehova as a smiling busybody, Moskvin as a pugnacious party with a single leg, and the entire first line of the company who were not cast for speaking rôles etching individual portraits of a small town's rank and file for the sake of startling realistic illusion. Now, there is a deep undercurrent of realistic truth in the mob of "Lysistrata," but it is a realism in which the individual is lost in the crowd instead of standing out from it. Unity of rhythm is the major consideration—not the unity of a military drill but the spiritual unity embracing wide variance in tempo and body plastic which has always made the ensemble of the Russian Ballet in its own home so thrilling and contagious a spectacle. To cite this break with the Art Theatre's traditions is enough; to decide between the two methods is by the way, for each is shrewdly devised to suit the dramatic task in hand.

I do not propose, either, to enter into a discussion of the merits of the controversial issues with which "Lysistrata" bristles, although it is interesting to recognize them and note how they are still alive today. It is one of those rare plays or works of art of any kind which are deliberate propaganda and yet at the same time great art. Like Bernard Shaw, Aristophanes wrote to correct or to ridicule a contemporary wrong. The wrong considered in "Lysistrata" was war— fratricidal war between the States of Greece. For that reason, it has been annexed by the Pacifists, who seem to forget that Lysistrata urged peace in the household that Greece might be strong enough to resist foreign aggression. To accomplish her aim, she recruited the women of all Greece and gave them the first recorded lesson in "women's rights." And for this reason, "Lysistrata" has been the Bible of the suffrage organizations, such as the Women's Political Union, which sponsored a production in the Brookside (N. Y.) open-air theatre in 1912 and two matinees in Maxine Elliott's Theatre, February 17 and 18, 1913. So far as I know, these are the only performances "Lysistrata" has had in America. The controversial vitality still inherent in the play is apparent again in Anthony M. Ludovici's choice of "Lysistrata" as a title for his recent stormy monograph on "woman's

future and future woman," one of the most discussed volumes in Dutton's "Today and Tomorrow Series," which has
already provoked rejoinder in another volume of the same
series, "Hypatia," by Dora (Mrs. Bertrand) Russell. In
seizing upon Aristophanes' heroine as prototype of the
future matriarch whom he fears, Ludovici ignores the fact
that Lysistrata did not bother her head about politics, peace
and procreation until the men of Greece had made a sorry
mess of things. If "Lysistrata" signifies sex tyranny, the
men of the world have only themselves to blame!

Still another storm center in which "Lysistrata" has fig-
ured and probably will continue to figure in our modern self-
conscious world of taboos and inhibitions, is the tilt between
prudes and free-thinkers. Aristophanes discusses the fundamental facts of life, love and sex with a frankness that out-
does the bed-room farceurs but with an honesty that renders
him spotless in comparison. The viewpoint of the straight-
laced is thus voiced by Benjamin Bickley Rogers in the introduction to his carefully "purified" translation: "It is much
to be regretted that the phallus-element should be so conspicuous in the present Play; for, in other respects, there are
few dramas—ancient or modern—which contain more noble
sentiments or more poetic beauty." What Dr. Rogers and
his fellows fail to comprehend in their prejudice is that
Aristophanes, for all his grotesque comedy, has infused the
same downright nobility and the same poetic beauty into his
phallic episodes as into his scenes of moral indignation and
lyric fervor.

That Nemirovitch-Dantchenko and his associates would
not fail to comprehend this fact, might have been foreseen

"LYSISTRATA"

Costume Sketches by Isaac Rabinovitch

by those who know the Dionysian fervor of the modern Russian stage. To cover the case of the Musical Studio's "Lysistrata," I need only quote, with the logical revisions, what I said in "The Russian Theatre" about "Salome" at the Kamerny Theatre:

"There is something about the honesty, the sincerity, the singleness of purpose of producers and players that keeps their interpretation free from anything but the most austere tragic reaction." Or the most chaste and salutary comic reaction. "They have achieved tragedy"—or comedy—"not by restraint but by self-effacing unrestraint. . . . The entire performance is intensely impersonal and at the same time hotly and passionately intimate,—a paradox which is possible only with artists and with audiences who view their art honestly."

CHAPTER IX

Spanish Passion—and Russian

back to mérimée for a new "carmen"

If "Lysistrata" revealed the Musical Studio as a pro-
digious adolescent, brimming with the wine of life, "Carmencita and the Soldier," at its premiere a year later, June
16, 1923, marked a bold step forward into a dynamic, defiant
and competent maturity. Scorning old law and seeming at
first glance to live without law, the regisseur and his company prove, on inquiry into the sources of the amazing effects
they achieve, to be working under new laws which they have
made themselves or rediscovered from a forgotten past.
"Carmencita and the Soldier" probably represents the nearest
possible approach to the Synthetic Theatre by the path of
reworking old material. Operetta and antique comedy had
served their turn; the next logical step was into the purlieus
of grand opera; and the director of the studio chose the
masterpiece of Georges Bizet, not only for its obvious, explicit and positive virtues but also for its latent possibilities.

What Nemirovitch-Dantchenko saw in "Carmen"—its
eternal qualities as well as the blemishes that challenged his
remolding hand—is succinctly expressed in an interview he
gave to *The Life of Art* a fortnight before the premiere:

"A lyric tragedy—that must be the ideal of this production. The composer Bizet remains the keynote where he

brilliantly and dramatically translates into music the intense characters and scenes of Mérimée's novel. But those portions of his work which were called forth by the demands of the public of his time have been adapted by the Musical Studio, changed root and branch or omitted entirely. Entire scenes have been shifted, the locale has been externalized. The fundamental theme of this lyric tragedy, as I see it, is the pathetic collision of elemental passions—the divine element of woman in Carmencita, the divine element of man in José. That theme must be set free from the surrounding triviality and operatic absurdity and must be developed with highest seriousness, passion, economy of external stage means and the depth of their inner expression."

In sum, the regisseur determined to discard the tinsel and trumpery in which "Carmen," the opera, was swathed at birth, as well as all the other false excrescences which had become attached to it through the last half century by the whims of prima donnas, from Gallie-Marié and Calvé down to Garden and Farrar, and by the rivalry of impresarios from Paris to Milan and Moscow and New York who vied with each other for bigger and brighter "Carmens." Back to the intimacy, simplicity and intensity of the original "Carmen," the "Carmen" of Prosper Mérimée and of Bizet's first unbridled dream! Passionate intensity—Spanish passion, first recorded by French passion, and now rekindled and fanned to consuming frenzy by Russian passion. That is the touchstone of "Carmencita and the Soldier." The passionate intensity of José and Carmencita when they love; the equal intensity of their hatred. The intensity of the essential struggle between male and female.

[107]

To achieve this passionate intensity, Nemirovitch-Dantchenko has pressed into service every lesson he learned in his earlier productions, every contributory element of the Synthetic Theatre—not for the sake of innovation but in the service of artistic truth. The Meilhac-Halévy libretto blocked his path to the heart of Mérimée-Bizet. He discarded it and commanded a wholly new one from the Russian poet, Constantin Lipskeroff. The new libretto didn't register with Bizet's score. He commissioned his conductor and musical adviser, Vladimir Bakaleynikoff, to revise and reorchestrate that score. To insure the verdict, "This is Spain!" as emphatically as "Lysistrata" had startled spectators into exclaiming "This is Greece!" he retained Isaac Rabinovitch to provide the architectural visualization. And finally, as his own personal contribution, he restored the chorus to the unobtrusive yet dominant rôle of aloof, impersonal and fateful commentary on the action, the rôle it had played in the Greek theatre—and had lost for over two thousand years!

To carry out these audacious innovations, the regisseur drew on three sources of inspiration—Mérimée, Bizet and Nietzsche. The most casual acquaintance with "Carmen," the story, will show how ample a warrant Nemirovitch-Dantchenko had in Mérimée himself for his interpretation. Here is no loose combination of melodrama and street fair, such as operatic audiences have had to put up with for fifty years, but a tale, half-way between short story and novel in length, with the concentration of the former and the broad human sweep of the latter, a tale of such poignant tragic power, such frankness of characterization and such profound

CARMENCITA, IN "CARMENCITA AND THE SOLDIER"
Costume plate by Isaac Rabinovitch

insight into the ways of destiny that the reader is left meek
and speechless at the end. Those who know "Carmen" only
from the stage do not know "Carmen." It is to be hoped
that the return of the Russians to the original story, for
confidence, sustenance and example, will rescue it from com-
parative neglect by readers today.

That Bizet's impulse in selecting Mérimée's story for lyric
treatment was characterized by genuine respect for its stark
tragic power, can not be doubted by those who have read his
letters to his friends at the time the idea occurred to him.
That he compromised this respect in order to get a hearing
at all in a world to whom Wagner was still anathema, is a
matter of history. That he retained as much of that respect
as possible, is conceivably the chief reason why the music of
"Carmen" has entered more deeply into the affections of the
entire world than the work of any other composer of the
last fifty years. "Bizet," wrote Saint-Saëns on the death of
his fellow-artist, "sought above all passion and life." And
these lines, written by Henry Malherbe in *Le Figaro* last
spring on the occasion of the fiftieth jubilee of "Carmen" at
the Opéra-Comique, sound almost prophetic if, as is likely,
the author had not heard of the project in Moscow:

"If anyone should care to strip this colorful, nervous and
exciting music of all that gratified the spectators of yesterday, lovers of the tinsel opéra-comique, he would find himself
in the presence of a realistic masterpiece vigorously and
frankly executed. What is to be found there of novelty,
motion and intensity recompenses us"—though not the Russians, with their intolerance of sham—"for the pretentious-
ness of certain episodes according to the fashion of its period.

For, in order to guard against being too original, Georges Bizet did not dare, even in 'Carmen,' to cry out too strongly against the accredited superstitions. To get his system received he was obliged to temporize. Necessity did not allow him to apply directly the principles of his liberal grammar of art. By the end of 1867, however, the great composer, without fully understanding his own genius, knew what he wanted to do. After the first performance of 'La Jolie Fille de Perth,' he wrote: 'I have made, this time, concessions which I swear that I regret. The school of couplets, of trills and of fables is dead, quite dead. Let us bury it without tears, without regret, without emotion. And forward!' "

That school, however, was not so dead as he hoped. Though he moved forward, wrangling with Du Locle, director of the Opéra-Comique, and agreeing to broader compromises on the part of the librettists than he would accept for the score, he still fell far short of his dream. To have his compromises, wrung from him in blood, damned as still too radical, as they were by many of the critics, must have been bitterly discouraging, although the legend that the cool reception of "Carmen" hastened his untimely death has been confuted.

It is this half-achieved "Carmen," of course, that has come down undimmed through five decades, growing rather than receding in popular favor and critical esteem, bursting national and racial boundaries, enlisting the talents and the genius of such a gallery of prima donnas as few rôles in the entire operatic repertory can boast, creating rivalries and discussions that have consumed thousands of columns of newspaper space. If Bizet had been permitted to write "Car-

LUCAS, THE MATADOR, IN "CARMENCITA AND THE SOLDIER"
Costume plate by Isaac Rabinovitch

men" as he dreamed it, with the sting of honesty and reality in it rather than the teasing of artificiality, how much more potent might have been its influence!

Bizet, then, the real Bizet, the thwarted Bizet, gave Nemirovitch-Dantchenko his second source of inspiration. The third was Nietzsche. With his uncanny instinct for penetrating to the heart of things, the philosopher, who narrowly missed being a composer himself, saw in "Carmen" the intense lyric tragedy that Bizet would have written—saw in actual performance only the evidences of that tragedy which survived the ordeal of compromise, and forthwith completed them. In a very real sense, therefore, the Russian version is even more directly and intimately beholden to Nietzsche's stimulating and revealing vision than to either Mérimée or Bizet. His close responsibility prompts the quotation of those lines from "The Case of Wagner" which served Nemirovitch-Dantchenko most dynamically:

"Yesterday—would you believe it?—I heard Bizet's masterpiece for the twentieth time. . . . His music seems to me perfect. It comes forward lightly, gracefully, stylishly. It is lovable, it does not sweat. 'All that is good is easy, everything divine runs with light feet'; this is the first principle of my esthetics. This music is wicked, refined, fatalistic: and withal remains popular,—it possesses the refinement of a race, not of an individual. It is rich. It is definite. It builds, organizes, completes: and in this sense it stands as a contrast to the polypus in music, to 'endless melody.' Have more painful, more tragic accents ever been heard on the stage before? And how are they obtained? Without gri-

[111]

maces! Without counterfeiting of any kind! Free from the lie of the grand style! . . .

"What Bizet's work has above all else is that which belongs to sub-tropical zones—that dryness of atmosphere, that *limpidezza* of the air. Here in every respect the climate is altered." (From the "damp north" and "the fog of the Wagnerian ideal.") "Here another kind of sensuality, another kind of sensitiveness and another kind of cheerfulness make their appeal. This music is gay, but not in a French or German way. Its gayety is African; fate hangs over it, its happiness is short, sudden, without reprieve. I envy Bizet for having had the courage of this sensitiveness, which hitherto in the cultured music of Europe has found no means of expression,—of this southern, tawny, sunburnt sensitiveness. . . . What a joy the golden afternoon of its happiness is to us! When we look out, with this music in our minds, we wonder whether we have ever seen the sea so calm. . . . How, for once, even our insatiability gets sated by its lascivious melancholy!— And finally love, love translated back into Nature! . . . Love as fate, as a fatality, cynical, innocent, cruel,—and precisely in this way Nature! The love whose means is war, whose very essence is the mortal hatred between the sexes!—I know no case in which the tragic irony which constitutes the kernel of love, is expressed with such severity, or in so terrible a formula, as in the last cry of Don José."

And again in the margin of Nietzsche's private copy of the score, against the "Habanera": "This is Eros as the Greeks imagined him, bitterly demonic and untamed. This

THE GYPSIES DRUG THE ADJUTANT WHILE CARMENCITA AWAITS JOSE
Scene from Act Two

THE SONG OF THE MATADOR, LUCAS
In Act Three, Scene One

"CARMENCITA AND THE SOLDIER"

NEMIROVITCH-DANTCHENKO HAS REVIVED THE ANCIENT GREEK CHORUS AS IMPER-
SONAL AND FATEFUL COMMENTARY ON THE ACTION

JOSÉ PLAYS DICE WITH THE GYPSIES. A VIVID PROOF THAT THE MUSICAL STUDIO
HAS INHERITED ITS PARENT'S MASTERY IN MAKEUP

TWO GROUPS FROM "CARMENCITA AND THE SOLDIER"

must be performed by a real witch. I know of nothing resembling this song."

The choice of a poet to fulfill the challenge of Mérimée, to complete the lost dream of Bizet, to realize the instinctive vision of Nietzsche, was no easy task. Furthermore, few themes in the realm of music, the theatre or letters have gathered round them the literary and critical galaxy that is the lot of "Carmen." Born of George Borrow, whose two gypsy classics, "The Zincali" and "The Bible in Spain," at least prompted Mérimée to go to the peninsula and see for himself, the Carmen legend was completed in its first form by Mérimée in 1845. Thirty years later came the libretto for Bizet's score by Henri Meilhac and Ludovic Halévy, notable figures in French literature for all their trifling with Mérimée. Less than a decade afterwards, the name of Nietzche was added to the rôle. Théophile Gautier wrote a poem, "Carmen," in which occur the lines worthy of Mérimée's conception:

> *"Les femmes disent qu'elle est laide,*
> *Mais tous les hommes en sont fous:*
> *Et l'archevêque de Tolède*
> *Chante la messe à ses genoux."*

Arthur Pougin and Charles Pigot are among the French critics who have written voluminously on the subject. Henry Hamilton, an English playwright, made a dramatic version of the story for the use of Olga Nethersole. American critics who have contributed notably to the "Carmen" literature include Philip Hale, who wrote the introduction to the Ditson edition of the score published in

1914, and Carl Van Vechten, whose chapter, "From George Borrow to Mary Garden," in his volume, "The Music of Spain," unfortunately out of print, summarizes both history and legend in lively vein. Finally—without attempting a bibliography—it is not generally known that Joseph Conrad often considered adapting one of his stories into a lyric drama and that "Carmen" was to have been its prototype. John Galsworthy has written of Conrad: " 'Carmen' was in the nature of a vice with him as with myself."

It is no wonder, then, that Nemirovitch-Dantchenko considered long and carefully the problem of the right poet for the new Russian version. The choice fell fortunately on Constantin Lipskeroff, born in Moscow in 1899 of a literary family, perhaps the sole inheritor in the present generation of the classic Russian lyric tradition which stems from Pushkin. Color, romance, depth of feeling, formal perfection, absorption in the philosophy of the Orient—these are the qualities that belong in common to him and his literary forebears. Four volumes of verse—"Sand and Roses," "Poems of Turkestan," "The Golden Palm" and "The Sixth Day"; a novel in verse, "Another One," dealing with the ominous atmosphere of Moscow on the eve of the Revolution; and two plays, "The Ocean Pea" and "Carmencita and José," an earlier dramatic form of "Carmen," preceded his "Carmencita and the Soldier."

Mere rehabilitation of the stilted lyric verses of the Meilhac-Halévy libretto, it may be guessed, would not have satisfied the regisseur. If further justification for a more rigorous course is asked in addition to that which I have already cited, perhaps the French critic, Henry Malherbe, may be called to the stand again: "If this great musician (Bizet) had lived, I do not doubt that he would have eliminated from his score the passages which lacked energy and color. This masterpiece that Bizet had conceived so warmly would have been without blemish and of the first order." Alteration of the score would have meant alteration of the libretto and its consequent regeneration. The Russians have merely reversed this process. Lipskeroff's renovation is thorough-going, drastic. How essentially new and his own —and Mérimée's—is "Carmencita and the Soldier," English readers will be able to make up their minds from the intense, passionate and picturesque translation by George S. and Gilbert Seldes. Witness these lines of José in place of the circus parades at the beginning of the first act:

> The eagles soar high
> O'er the hills of Navarra.
> In the tongue of Navarra
> Words are as music.
> The girls of Navarra
> Are as fierce as the mountains—
> Mates of the eagles for the boldest of hunters,
> Mates of the eagles for the boldest of hunters.
> Girls in plenty,
> And plenty of lads.

Or these lashing lines of Carmencita to the strains of the "Habanera":

> Never did God or Devil sing
> A sweeter song than mine.
> The way to Heaven hurts my feet—
> Come, Devils, keep me company.

[115]

Desire is seeking for its mate.
Forget, my friend, bow down your head.
Many have found their way to death,
Here in my enchanting arms.
Come to me, I call you, come!

The text is too full of lines and phrases that strike home
with brilliant imagery, tragic power and lightning-like characterization to permit further quotation. Besides, the
broader alterations in the structure are more important.
From the first curtain to the last, a surging, driving demon
carries the action relentlessly to its dénouement. Without
beating the bushes or indulging in lyrical small talk until
late diners have arrived, the prophetic and impersonal chorus
utters its warning to José; Carmencita enters, spins her
web, departs into the Colonel's house; José's mother, in
reality his subconscious memory of her, repeats the warning
through the medium of three women of the chorus; sounds
of the quarrel emerge from the house, the chorus with
second sight follows it, rapt; Carmencita, her victim and
the guests pour out of the door; the gypsy is bound, starts
her teasing game of alluring the peasant soldier, who resists,
at first stolidly, then with difficulty, and finally yields.

The second act plunges onward with equal impetus. Into
the smugglers' den, Carmencita's retreat, comes an adjutant;
he is drugged and put out of the way; drawn by the fatal
lure, José arrives, torn between duty and desire; the gypsy
caresses, he stiffens; the gypsy scorns him, he relents; the
adjutant, still in stupor, returns, only to fall dead on José's
dagger; the die is cast, José stays, gypsy; what is the next
foray?

Carmencita (Olga Baklanova) Tries to Lure José (Ivan Velikanoff) to Remain with Her

A Scene from Act Two

Misail Speransky as Lucas, the Matador, and Olga Baklanova as Carmencita

THE TRAGIC TRIANGLE OF "CARMENCITA AND THE SOLDIER"

PYOTR SARATOVSKY AS LUCAS, THE ERSTWHILE ESCAMILLO   OLGA BAKLANOVA AS CARMENCITA

MATADOR AND GYPSY IN "CARMENCITA AND THE SOLDIER"

The third act is in two scenes: One a mere episode, a picture, a snap-shot—the matador, Lucas. The other, again in the gypsy den, distills in ominous contrast the casual life of the contrabandists and Carmencita reading her fate in candle drippings, followed by the tottering of passion and the confrontal of José and Lucas.

The last act is keyed at a blinding pitch. Here the chorus becomes the protagonist, and the tragedy races to its doom. "I go first; you—next!" And so it is—as the matador's song sounds in the distance:

> A stormy life is a glorious boon,
> Even the death-blow of love is sweet.
> There is no joy or passion that consumes
> Like the heat in the thick of the fight.
> Then let the death-knell ring,
> The knell of love,
> The boon of stormy life.

In this new "Carmen," then, we see that Micaëla, the original librettists' sop to the sentimentality of fifty years ago, drops out altogether; her portions of the score are allotted to three women in the chorus singing for José's mother, an all-pervading figure in José's subconscious mind, according to Mérimée. Old Dorotea, the smuggler, reënters the cast from Mérimée's pages; and the bull-fighter regains his true name, Lucas. The interruptions of an extraneous ballet are suppressed; dancing, where the continuously rhythmic and plastic expression of the human body reaches that formal state, is invariably motivated by the action. Even vocal expression is subordinated to the action when

[117]

the minimum of attention required by the singing voice would halt, retard or falsify the action. Much of Bizet's familiar music, therefore, becomes accompaniment, atmospheric and emotional background, to pantomime—Moscow Art Theatre pantomime. And the result of this expedient, which has been called mimo-drama in its more extended use in parts of "Love and Death," is akin, of course, to the most vivid moments of the Russian Ballet in the hands of Mordkin or Nizhinsky. It is well that Lipskeroff was chosen for the task. Only a poet, in the first place, could have grasped and carried out Nemirovitch-Dantchenko's bold and difficult conception. Only a poet with Lipskeroff's mastery of form and sensitive ear could have coördinated every line of his text, every link in his action, with the musical phrases of Bizet.

In the flutter over the new libretto and the reorchestration, three major factors in both the artistic and the popular success of "Carmencita and the Soldier" must not be neglected: Rabinovitch, the designer; Baklanova and the players; the regisseur and his chorus.

Generally speaking, Rabinovitch faced the same problem as in "Lysistrata" and he solved it in the same manner—complete utilization of the stage space, architecturally speaking, through dynamic interplay between the setting and the action. Specifically, however, as Efros points out, he was concerned with volume and height instead of with transparency and depth, as in the Greek comedy. Furthermore, in place of infinite variety through his pivoting Hellas, he chose a solid, substantial, constructivist mass of arches and balconies and stairs, mounting upward unbelievably, which serve for one locale after another under the wizardry of light. We shall see presently how this setting is both the master and the servant of the action in the case of the chorus. Here is not a mere glimpse of Spain, a cross section of its life, but its symbolic epitome. And color rounds out the quintessentials of architecture: Red, yellow, black; red, yellow, black; the blended effect of old gold, of ochred stucco—not to the end of copying Spanish dress and the Spanish landscape but to underscore the leading motives of Spanish character: Passion smoldering, ready to flame at a spark.

If I have said little of the talents and achievements of Olga Baklanova in the preceding chapters—not so much, in fact, as I devoted in "The Russian Theatre" to her work as a novice in the Dramatic Company—it may be attributed to the fact that her leaping emotional and romantic gifts are at home in the Musical Studio, fit into the ensemble, are taken for granted, while in the atmosphere of the Dramatic Company the contrast with her surroundings drew unusual attention to her. As Carmencita, however, Baklanova once more rivets attention on her prowess in passionate portrayal. Her gypsy is neither wicked, sly, scheming nor flirtatious. She is a lithe and willful tigress, a handsome animal, conscious of her power, but applying it by instinct rather than by calculation. She is what she is, by grace of God, without the slightest conception that she might be otherwise. Hence, her slavery to superstition, her abject horror at the omen of her doom in the candle drippings, her unmoved and fatalistic acceptance of that doom, her ecstasy in love, her loathing in hatred. Less highly-hued but equally right and brilliant in

[119]

conception and execution is the José of Ivan Velikanoff—a stolid, well-meaning peasant lad whose hidden emotions are kindled by the gypsy, who is always miles behind her swifter passions and who improvidently burns his bridges to a safe past only when she is beginning to tire of him. That the tortoise catches up with the hare in the end is only one of Mérimée's fatalistic ironies that gives the clew to regisseur and singing-actor for this unconventional interpretation. Two such sharply-etched protagonists, of course, set a pace that the eager young players of the studio are quick to follow, and the taut and hidden thread of passionate intensity carries through to the least member of the ensemble.

Perhaps the most revolutionary expedient, however, which Nemirovitch-Dantchenko hit upon to achieve his desired intensity is his handling of the chorus. The first reports of this production to reach this country seemed to indicate a similarity to the mise en scène of "Le Coq d'Or" at the Metropolitan Opera House—a chorus, attired in black, which sings but does not act; actors who perform only in pantomime; principal characters with duplicate interpreters performing these separate functions. A second's glance at "Carmencita and the Soldier" destroys all thought of a parallel between the two productions. True, Nemirovitch-Dantchenko segregates his chorus from the action, ranges it on Rabinovitch's Spanish balconies above it. But both chorus and principals act and sing and are similarly costumed. What the founder of the Musical Studio has accomplished is to revive the Greek chorus as omniscient commentary on the action, as—in Nietzsche's paraphrase of Schiller's Preface to "The Bride of Messina"—"a living wall which tragedy draws round herself to guard her from contact with the world of reality, and to preserve her ideal domain and poetical freedom." In concentrated emotional power, he has even bettered the Greek chorus, whose backs were probably turned to the audience, for his Spanish chorus uses its eyes as the most potent engine in concentrating the attention of the audience on the action below. The chorus of "Carmencita and the Soldier" is a shrewd and superbly executed capitalization of the phenomenon of the crowd on the street corner luring your eye to a performing plane or a dare-devil painting a skyscraper's flagpole.

What has been the verdict on this intrepid experiment? Violently for—and against. Hostility, however, has been limited chiefly to those purists and fundamentalists who lose their temper when a great conductor alters a single crescendo in a classic symphony; who insist on Shakespeare being played—not, strangely enough, as he was written—but as they saw him played in their youth; who—but why dwell on so familiar a type! One hundredth part of the changes the Russians have made would alienate this spectator. Next, there is the cautious kind who honestly believe that "Carmen" is a superb example of a mannered and artificial type of French opera and who would rather let it go at that than see it improved. Finally, there are those who approach "Carmencita and the Soldier" on its intrinsic merits—as if there had never been a "Carmen." This, it seems to me, is the only fair way. And, as proof of the probable results if this way be followed, I am taking the liberty of quoting in its entirety the altogether amazing criticism of the

[121]

production from the pen of Alfred Kerr, of the *Berliner Tageblatt:*

I

"The musicians have spoken. (About the Russian opera). They are right. . . . A friend says: 'Wouldn't you like to go? There's a dramatic side to it, too.'

"So I saw Nemirovitch-Dantchenko again, who had come to Berlin before with Stanislavsky, of esteemed memory. We talk. He is quite pale and terse.

"Now the secret is out.

II

"Is this a shed? Or a courtyard? Or a cigarette factory in Seville?

"No. . . . The theoretical stage. Theoretical arches, theoretical balconies, theoretical steps,—what was done before by Meyerhold; then copied by us . . . and set aside. Poles here and there; heights, depths; balconies; stairs; stairs . . . at first a bit sad.

III

"The soldier. (Once Caruso sang him). Above, the chorus, sprinkled about, indulged, all over everywhere; at most, only one, two Spanish girls on the same spot. Very good picture; yes, something between Goya, Manet, Picasso.

"Still, it seems to me: if the chorus is to be unreal, that is, only imagined—then it should have been detached by a veil from the lower, real reality. . . .

[122]

IV

"Now the love pangs.

"It goes on. From beyond is wafted . . . an inexpressible magic. Again I am altogether with you, Russians—something always trembles joyfully when you play theatre.

"Here is no opera; the dull gesture is lacking. Everything in its quintessence. That's the way it should be. Everything; anguished soul between man and woman—with music. That's what it is.

V

"Nobody nods or fidgets in the parquet. The audience is tense. Details put aside. The players stand rather than walk about. (Groups). And if they have much to do, they are spared singing for a while—then the orchestra sings their songs.

"Only the dramatic . . . with music. With the transposed, mangled, cut-up, changed—and yet in spite of everything—always Bizet-ish music.

VI

"In my whole life, none the less, this music has never so deeply entered into my consciousness. One hears it—with more hypnotic effect.

"Bizet is scalped, castrated, massacred, in fact, extended. . . . No, Nemirovitch-Dantchenko tells me: "Bizet now comes into his own, he had made a concession to his librettists against his will, he wanted Mérimée rather than Meilhac-Halévy . . .

"Here he has him: in all his brute force.

[123]

VII

"A French lady, and so a countrywoman of Bizet's, said, dumbfounded: 'Extraordinary: of all the 'Carmen' productions I have seen, I've never been so thrilled . . . as today!'

"And the same thing goes for me.

"And the final why?—These are not singers, who act. They are actors, who sing.

"Everything diffuse is missing: everything constraining the dramatic kernel is banned.

VIII

"Bizet is scalped, castrated, massacred, sabotaged, extended . . . The principle is false.

"The result is right."

CHAPTER X

By Way of Promise

IN institutional playhouses like the Moscow Art Theatre, and especially in a branch like the Musical Studio, which is still building up its repertory, the laboratory contains a number of productions in various stages of completion. At the present moment, an invoice of the Musical Studio's workshop reveals: "Love and Death," a triple bill drawn by three different composers from the works of Russia's greatest poet, Alexander Pushkin, which had its dress rehearsal on the closing night of last season and which has not yet been given before a public audience; "A Nobleman's Nest," a lyric drama taken from Turgenieff's novel with score by Vladimir Rebikoff, which the Soviet censorship has prohibited; "Boris Godunoff," in a version restoring the original score and libretto by Musorgsky, which had its first rehearsal while I was in Moscow; and an anthology of the songs and ballads of the Russian *muzhik,* gathered in the villages and preserved with authentic peasant costumes and interpretation.

Each of these projects, besides being intrinsically interesting, illustrates some custom, obstacle or motive typical of the life of the Musical Studio. The performance of "Love and Death," for instance, before an invited and exacting audience on the last night of the season represents a

[125]

time-honored tradition not only of the Musical Studio but of the Art Theatre itself. Frequently in the past a new production has had its virtual premiere in May, June or July, although the public has no opportunity to see it until fall, when the rough spots and the mistakes disclosed at the dress rehearsal have been corrected during a summer's patient labor. "A Nobleman's Nest," in turn, reveals the same inexplicable censorship at work which issued the ban on the plays of Tchehoff. "Boris Godunoff" not only embodies the Art Theatre's precept of thorough preparation, having been in rehearsal already for almost a year, but it also proves the contention that I made in the chapter on "Carmencita and the Soldier"—that innovation for its own sake is not the policy of the Musical Studio and that Nemirovitch-Dantchenko is just as ready to restore a superb original that has been lost through misdirected zeal as he is to discard those elements of an original work which dissipate its significance today. Finally, the pains that have been taken by the regisseur and his associates to collect the songs of the Russian soil before the inroads of an industrial age destroy them, proves that the Musical Studio has its feet firmly planted in the rich loam of folk art, despite some of its esoteric flights.

Inasmuch as I saw in Moscow only one of the early rehearsals of Rachmaninoff's "Aleko," the opening number of "Love and Death," and am not one of those fortunate individuals who can visualize emotionally a work of art without standing in its completed presence, I can report only documentarily on this fifth production of the Musical Studio. Nemirovitch-Dantchenko, I know, considers "Love

RACHMANINOFF'S "ALEKO"
Text by Vladimir Nemirovitch-Dantchenko
From Pushkin's Poem, "The Gypsies"

and Death" as a whole the nearest approach he has yet made toward his goal of the Synthetic Theatre. I suspect that he means that in this trio of short lyric dramas, linked not only by their common source in Pushkin but also in their varying treatment of the theme indicated by the title, he has found it possible to combine the elements of music, poetry and the plastic body in more nearly equal portions than at any time in the Musical Studio's preceding history and that he has achieved thereby a total effect farther outweighing the sum total of the parts than ever before.

"Aleko," which introduces the program of "Love and Death," is a passionately intense lyric drama in one act and two scenes which Sergei Rachmaninoff and Nemirovitch-Dantchenko wrote in their youth. A third great figure in Russian art, the composer Anton Arensky, was its godfather. One day in 1891 as Rachmaninoff, aged eighteen, was about to be graduated from the Moscow Conservatory, his master, Arensky, sought out Nemirovitch-Dantchenko, already at the age of thirty-three a commanding figure as a novelist, a playwright and a critic of music and drama. "I have three pupils in composition," said Arensky, "for whom I wish librettos. I want you to do the one for Rachmaninoff." Nemirovitch-Dantchenko turned to Pushkin, as more than one hard-pressed figure in the Russian theatre has done in an emergency during the last hundred years. Taking up the poem, "The Gypsies," he dramatized it in three days and sent the manuscript to the young student-composer. A month later Rachmaninoff had finished the score and with it won the conservatory's gold medal. Two years later, Safonoff, director of the conservatory, arranged for the performance of the gypsy dances from "Aleko." Since then it has been played in its entirety not only at the Great State Theatre in Moscow and at the Marinsky in Petersburg, but all over Russia, with Chaliapin appearing on occasion in the rôle of Aleko.

With its scene laid in the Romany camps of Bessarabia, "Aleko" recounts on the lips of the Old Gypsy the faithlessness of Zemfira's mother; in sharp, vivid, tragic action the faithlessness of Zemfira herself; and in swift lightning strokes of verbal thrust and flashing knife, the bitter disillusionment of Aleko, the Russian, the wanderer, who finds no freedom even in the irresponsible life of the *tsiganie*. Both the music and the episodes stab to the heart of the situation with only a minimum of atmospheric accompaniment or preparation. That minimum, in turn, prepares the spectator for the ominous mood of the brooding plains. That portions of the love songs are rather conventional is not surprising in a composer of eighteen. The authentic folk-feeling and technical dexterity and thematic originality of treatment of the gypsy dances, however, are unmistakable sign-posts to the world-wide fame which awaited the young Rachmaninoff.

Like many of the great products of Russian creative artists, "Aleko" has a philosophical undercurrent that a westerner may easily lose, enthralled by its absorbing action. That undercurrent, by the wheel of chance, probably means more today than at any time since Pushkin penned his poem. Nor is Nemirovitch-Dantchenko, with Rachmaninoff at hand to make the point more poignant, the first Russian man of letters to detect its deep significance. For two generations ago, Fyodor Dostoievsky wrote these lines in the course of his study of Pushkin, published in "Pages from the Journal of an Author," in the translation by S. Koteliansky and J. Middleton Murry:

"Already, in the character of Aleko, the hero of 'The Gypsies,' is exhibited a powerful, profound, and purely Russian idea, later to be expressed in harmonious perfection in 'Yevgeny Onyegin,' where almost the same Aleko appears, not in a fantastic light, but as tangible, real, and comprehensible. In Aleko Pushkin had already discovered, and portrayed with genius, the unhappy wanderer in his native land, the Russian sufferer of history, whose appearance in our society, uprooted from among the people, was a historic necessity. The type is true and perfectly rendered; it is an eternal type, long since settled in our Russian land. These homeless Russian wanderers are wandering still, and the time will be long before they disappear. If they in our day no longer go to gypsy camps to seek their universal ideals in the wild life of the gypsies and their consolation away from the confused and pointless life of our Russian intellectuals, in the bosom of nature, they launch into Socialism, which did not exist in Aleko's day; they march with a new faith into another field, and there work zealously, believing, like Aleko, that they will by their fantastic occupations obtain their aims and happiness, not for themselves alone, but for all mankind. For the Russian wanderer can find his own peace only in the happiness of all men; he will not be more cheaply satisfied.

The other two numbers of "Love and Death"—"The Fountain of Bakhchi-Sarai" and "Cleopatra"—differ from

"Aleko" in possessing purely lyric without the additional social significance. "The Fountain" ties up with two Pushkin landmarks: Anton Arensky wrote it as Opus 46 in 1899, the hundredth anniversary of the poet's birth. Its first fully adequate interpretation was put in rehearsal last year along with "Aleko" and "Cleopatra" with a view to celebrating the hundred and twenty-fifth anniversary. But the Musical Studio has absorbed too much of the Art Theatre's traditional thoroughness to let calendar considerations take precedence over adequate preparation, and the premiere thereby carried over into 1925.

Student of Rimsky-Korsakoff but more nearly akin in spirit to Tchaikovsky and, as we have just noted, one of the masters of Rachmaninoff, Arensky adhered closely to the form and even the matchless and passionate lines of Pushkin's poem—much more closely, in fact, than did Nikita Balieff and his composer, Alexei Arhangelsky, in the version of the ballad which introduced the third program of the Chauve-Souris in New York in the autumn of 1922. The regisseur of the Musical Studio has chosen to retain Arensky's fluid and episodic form, seizing the opportunity to develop plastic action as eloquent aid to orchestra and voice.

The memory of tragedy springing from a triangle of unrequited love is the theme of "The Fountain." Still a third aspect of the cycle's title is disclosed in "Cleopatra," the mimo-drama which Reinhold Gliere has devised from an episode in Pushkin's novel, "Egyptian Nights," a subtle, mysterious and overpowering tale of the ruthless erotic whims of Nile's insatiable serpent.

It is even less satisfactory, without observing its action

RACHMANINOFF'S "ALEKO"
With Text by Vladimir Nemirovitch-Dantchenko, from Pushkin's Poem "The Gypsies"

A Costume Sketch by Ivan Gremislavsky and Nikolai Iznar

and hearing its score, to attempt description or appraisal of
"A Nobleman's Nest." This much is plausible: Inasmuch
as Turgenieff's novel deals realistically with a love episode
in a minor key between an unhappily married man and a
high-strung conscientious young girl, both of the upper
middle classes, Rebikoff has probably striven in his score
for such a mood as Tchehoff achieves in that memorable
third act of "The Cherry Orchard," where the music of the
orchestra, playing for the dance, makes its way into the fore-
ground now and then, only to recede to the rôle of atmospheric undertone. The natural course of Turgenieff's story,
with many of its episodes built round the pianoforte in the
music room and with one of its leading characters a pathetic
old German music teacher, provides ample motivation for
such treatment, while the composer of "The Christmas Tree"
and of the score for Ostrovsky's "The Storm" probably feels
wholly at home at his task and finds his material readily
susceptible to his theory that music is "the language of the
emotions" and therefore should be casual, without form.
Unless some feature not readily conceivable has entered into
this realistic lyric drama, the Soviet ban on it would seem
to have the same flimsy basis as the prohibition of Tchehoff.

By all odds the most provocative experiment still pent up
in the Musical Studio's laboratory is its projected production
of Modest Musorgsky's music drama of the Russian people,
"Boris Godunoff." In daring to storm this citadel of the
Russian opera, for the sake of giving his Musical Studio its
"final examination" and of proving its ultimate right to
exist, Nemirovitch-Dantchenko has elected to attack through
three gates. The frontal assault is directed against the main

[131]

entrance, guarded by Rimsky-Korsakoff; the right flank confronts the tower of the fortress held by Fyodor Chaliapin; while the left wing lies in ambush ready at a signal to leap up a difficult, forgotten and neglected footpath in the rocks.

Rimsky-Korsakoff's self-appointed guardianship of Musorgsky's memory is the center of one of the most earnest and heated debates in the contemporary lyric world. Musorgsky wrote "Boris" in the years 1868-70 to a libretto which he himself fashioned from Pushkin's original. The directors of the opera refused it and, listening to the advice of his friends, he spent the year of 1871 revising it and correcting the lack of feminine interest. Fragments were performed at the Marinsky Theatre in Petersburg in 1873 and the whole had its premiere on January 24, 1874. After twenty successive performances, attended by unheard-of enthusiasm crossed with equally extravagant indignation, the opera lapsed in the repertory. Musorgsky died in 1881. Five years later, with the best will in the world toward his friend's memory but with what appears now to be mistaken zeal, Rimsky-Korsakoff completed a drastic revision of the score to make it more palatable to conventional ears, considerably altered the libretto and superintended the revival of "Boris" in 1886. It is this version of the opera which Paris, London and New York and the Russian capitals themselves have heard for the last four decades, with the exception of slight revisions made by Rimsky himself shortly before his death.

In recent years, as the western world and Russia itself have come to realize that Musorgsky was the fountain head of contemporary Russian music, that he influenced Debussy

ALEKO DISCOVERS THAT ZEMFIRA NO LONGER LOVES HIM

THE TALE OF THE OLD GYPSY. ALEKO (ABOVE) LISTENS ENTHRALLED

TWO EPISODES FROM RACHMANINOFF'S "ALEKO"

Opening Number of "Love and Death," with Text by Nemirovitch-Dantchenko
Drawn from Pushkin

THE PRAYER OF THE PRIEST IN "CLEOPATRA"
From Pushkin's "Egyptian Nights"

OLGA BAKLANOVA AS ZAREMA
Surrounded by the Other Wives and Slaves of the Khan Girei in Pushkin's "The
Fountain of Bakhchi-Sarai"

TWO OF THE THREE ANGLES OF "LOVE AND DEATH"

directly and the work of Scriabin and Stravinsky indirectly, the suspicion has been growing that Rimsky-Korsakoff manhandled "Boris" and, for the sake of conventional approval, stripped Musorgsky's score of its disturbingly original qualities. The adherents of Rimsky and his course maintain that "Boris" in its first form was illiterate and impossible to perform and that wholesale revision alone could put it in service to the practical lyric stage. The opponents of this view, while admitting that Musorgsky was probably ahead of his time, insist that it is only fair to his memory as a pioneer to provide the opportunity for a new appraisal by ears that have reached far into hitherto uncharted territory in the last half century.

Acting on this latter conviction, several movements have developed, spontaneously and without mutual relationship, to give Musorgsky this new trial. The mails from London, for instance, have recently brought word of the projected republication by J. and W. Chester of an autographed score of "Boris" as it came from the press. Extant copies of this first edition are rare and guarded in private and state collections. Two Gallic musical authorities, Robert Godet and Aloys Mooser, have attempted the restoration of the score as well as a rehabilitation of the text, while the latter has been translated into English by M. C. H. Collet.

Prior to this project and independent of it, Nemirovitch-Dantchenko obtained the permission of the Soviet authorities in charge of the Musorgsky manuscripts and commissioned experts to go back of the first published edition, which is alleged to be full of printers' errors, to the virgin record of the composer's creative imagination. It is the result of their labors that the Musical Studio placed in rehearsal last December on an afternoon during my stay in Moscow. No orchestra; no scenery; no principals. Just the chorus, a piano and a pianist at one end of the long promenade foyer. They have in hand the opening ensemble—the populace bewailing the death of Tsar Fyodor. Pacing backwards and forwards, his hands behind his back, the regisseur listens, then interrupts: "Remember that you are peasants, that for you the light of the world has gone out. Musorgsky's music is a heaven-piercing wail. Don't be afraid to let yourself go —your voices, your bodies, everything!" And they did— with results that sent a thrill up the spine. It was a thrill I had never before experienced so early in "Boris," and I am not in a position to say whether it was due to the reversion to Musorgsky's own score or to a living interpretation of peasant woe in place of the usual deadly choral routine.

Coincident with the assault on the main gate, Nemirovitch-Dantchenko proposes to move against the Chaliapin tower. Not that he underrates the enormous and unique genius of Fyodor Ivanovitch's interpretation or that he misconstrues Chaliapin's motives. He is convinced that Musorgsky intended the crowd to be the hero rather than the Tsar, and he realizes that the warping of the opera is due, not to the willfulness of the great singer-actor, but to the vast spread between his masterful portrait and the weak ensemble surrounding him. In other words, he believes that he has a friend within the walls and that Chaliapin would be the first to commend his course. That course consists in presenting the opera as Musorgsky wrote it, with all parts in equally able hands, and in letting its leading figures emerge

"CLEOPATRA"
From Pushkin's "Egyptian Nights"
Costume Sketch by Ivan Gremislavsky and Nikolai Iznar

naturally and according to their human appeal. He hopes to develop not one Boris but two or more, just as the Dramatic Company had two supremely great and utterly different Tsar Fyodors, with two more of no mean caliber in reserve.

Finally there is the neglected path up through the rocks—the path of scenic interpretation. Admirers of Golovin and his gigantic settings of medieval pageant and tapestry will protest the phrase "neglected." But in the sense that Nemirovitch-Dantchenko understands the visual side of production since "Lysistrata" and "Carmencita and the Soldier"—as constructivist or architectural use of the stage space which will provide a mise en scène to react on the action and be reacted upon by it—the opportunities presented by "Boris" have been neglected. When I talked with him last winter, he had been working on the visual problem of "Boris" only two months. Many details remained to be settled. Even the general lines were subject to alteration. But at that time, seeing Musorgsky's masterpiece as the Tragedy of Power, the monumental and age-long tragedy of the Russian people, he intended to propose to his scenic designer the erection of a huge pyramidal structure with throne and altar at the top (the Monarchy linked with the Church), the boyars or princes in the medial levels, and the people, the peasants, at the great spreading base. Since the structure of the medieval Polish State was identical and in view of the fact that Musorgsky's original version with one or two minor exceptions has alternate scenes in Russia and Poland, the regisseur proposed to set the other half of his revolving stage as a great Polish pyramid, with Gothic motives to differentiate it from the Russian Byzantine.

Before we close the door on the Musical Studio's laboratory, it will pay us to glance briefly at the repertory of peasant songs which have been collected in the villages of Central Russia by Anna Tretyakova, attached for this purpose to the Studio's staff. Fearing that the industrial revolution, which is remaking Russia far faster than the social revolution, would obliterate all traces of this creative power among the Russian folk, this authority from the Institute of Musical Science went and lived with the *muzhiks* in their *izbas,* obtained phonographic records, observed the accompanying dramatic action, collected authentic peasant costumes and returned to Moscow to train the eager and adaptable members of the Musical Studio in the fruits of her research. The result, whether sung by the Studio's vocal quartet or by a larger ensemble, is a richness and fullness of atmosphere that has never been suspected by those who have heard and seen the professional adaptations of Russian peasant songs and dances in theatre and cabaret.

Whither, by way of still more distant promise, does the Moscow Art Theatre Musical Studio plan to chart its course? There remains the Italian opera. Then there is Wagner. Or Greek tragedy, if one can be found with a theme potent today. What Nemirovitch-Dantchenko awaits, however, is new creative work, written by poet and composer under the stimulus of the idea which he has embodied so vividly with makeshift material. The Synthetic Theatre calls, as the Ballet called, for its Stravinsky. Who will it be?

CHAPTER XI

THE SYNTHETIC THEATRE

A FREQUENTLY recurring phrase in the last few chapters
has been "the Synthetic Theatre." Beyond briefly defining
the significance of this term, as Nemirovitch-Dantchenko
understands it, I have preferred to let its full import develop
bit by bit in the concrete aspects of the Musical Studio's
expanding repertory. The time has come, however, for a
more extensive examination of this conception, its historic
background and its implications.

This deductive method of approach to the subject has had
its counterpart in the mental processes of Nemirovitch-Dantchenko himself. In the beginning, he ventured only a tenta-
tive criticism of the existing lyric stage, together with a very
general program for revitalizing it. Thereafter, the problems of each production were sufficient to the day of their
advent. Now, however, in the light of five years of experiment, he has deduced certain conclusions that may stand as
a platform, a manifesto, a confession of faith, a seven com-
mandments for the Synthetic Theatre:

Propounding the question, "What is necessary for the
reform of the art of the lyric stage?" he replies:

"To seek new forms for this art;

"To seek ways to combat the routine of the lyric stage
which has lost its theatrical conviction;

"To purge musical-dramatic expression of its rubber stamps, stencils and bad taste;

"To introduce into the field of lyric drama an atmosphere of genuine art and, first of all, the art of the actor;

"*To create a theatre of the musical actor.*

"It is necessary that this theatre should be a THEATRE and not a concert stage,—a theatre in whose structure the first place shall be held by the *actor*.

"And the principal equipment of this actor should be his musical and vocal qualities."

Once in the course of civilization, according to history, this ideal theatre, synthesizing all the arts and fusing them into one independent art, was realized—on the slopes of the Acropolis in the Theatre of Dionysus in Athens. Even before the Greek State fell, its culture and its theatre became decadent. And ever since, men have been trying in vain to recapture the secret of that culture, of that theatre. That they have never fully done so, however, either intuitively, by the process the Attic dramatists followed, or consciously, with the aid of artists, philosophers and scientists, is no proof that they never will. The last hundred years have seen more than one attempt barely fail to achieve complete success. We understand today better than ever before the fundamental elements of this Synthetic Theatre. And its attainment awaits the arrival of the artistic genius who can create in terms of those elements.

For over three centuries it has been apparent that spoken drama alone, no matter how it may satisfy certain normal human cravings, does not possess within itself both the flint and the tinder to rekindle the ecstatic mood of the Greek theatre. In that time many efforts have been made to mate drama, now with music, now with the plastic human body, in the hope that the offspring would resemble the long-lost child of Hellas. These two main procedures for fertilizing the drama have resulted roughly in the forms of artistic expression known as opera and ballet. Both methods, in fact, are applied simultaneously in ballet, with the second predominating. Opera and ballet, in turn, have been mated. But the solution to the problem seems as remote as ever.

Opera, even in the ablest hands, has never rung quite true. There is a flaw, a false thread, a note of artificiality, in its esthetic make-up. Paraphrasing the reactions of the young Wagner toward this form of expression, Ernest Newman has written: "The opera not only did not achieve the unity it professed to aim at; it did not even let either of its two great and ever-warring constituents tyrannize effectively over the other. Instead, each merely lamed the other; the average opera was neither a good play spoiled by music nor good music spoiled by a play, but merely a bad play and formless music adding each to the other's foolishness." With characteristically vivid imagery, the Russian critic, A. Kugel, puts the case thus: "Opera as such is nothing more nor less than an omelet of the arts of the theatre. The poetic subject floats in the butter of music. One is not connected with the other organically. The spectacle predominates over the psychology of the rôle. The music breaks up the unity of the spoken words. The words tear apart the transparent rainbow of the music."

Ballet, on the other hand, has a different flaw—the flaw

of incompleteness. Although in the hands of Mordkin and Diagileff it became a serious contender for consideration as an independent art, although at its peak in Stravinsky it fuses music and the plastic human form more successfully than any opera mates music and the spoken word, it still lacks the magic appeal of the spoken word. Ballet is the vision of the Greek theatre seen through a glass darkly.

Despite difficulties and discouragements, however, the quest goes on. To spur that quest, poets and philosophers from time to time confide in us their fleeting glimpse of the elusive ideal. Schiller, explaining the process by which he wrote his poetry, said: "The perception with me is at first without a clear and definite object; this forms itself later. A certain musical mood of mind precedes, and only after this does the poetical idea follow with me." Nietzsche, summarizing his analysis of the Greek theatre in "The Birth of Tragedy," wrote: "With the preëstablished harmony which obtains between perfect drama and its music, the drama attains the highest degree of conspicuousness, such as is usually unattainable in mere spoken drama. . . . Music is the adequate idea of the world, drama is but the reflex of this idea, a detached umbrage thereof."

And yet, clear as it may be to the intuition of poet and philosopher that music and the spoken word have a common lot far more exalted than the heritage of either alone, the mating process is beset with all but insuperable practical handicaps. Concerned particularly with Wagner's dilemma, Ernest Newman in "Wagner as Man and Artist" states the conditions of the general impasse: "Poetry and music are not the loving sisters that the fancy of the literary man

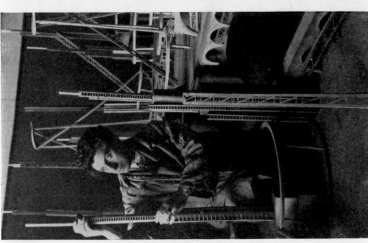

PIERRE KONTCHALOVSKY
Designer of "La Périchole"

ISAAC RABINOVITCH
Designer of "Lysistrata" and "Carmencita and the Soldier," at Work on a Model in His Studio

MARIA GORTINSKAYA
Designer of "The Daughter of Madame Angot"

THE SCENIC DESIGNERS OF THE MUSICAL STUDIO

PASSION PLUNGES TOWARD ITS DOOM IN "CARMENCITA AND THE SOLDIER"

José Slinks in the Shadowed Arch, Watching Jealously Lucas, the Matador, and Carmencita. Setting Designed by Isaac Rabinovitch

would make them out to be; they are rival goddesses, very jealous and intolerant of each other. The poet, in proportion as his work is genuine, faultless poetry, has no need of the musican. Music is cruel, ravenous, selfish, overbearing with poetry; it deprives it, for its own ends, of almost everything that makes it poetry, altering its verbal values, disregarding its rhymes, substituting another rhythm for that of the poet. It has no need of anything but the poetic idea, and to get at that kernel it ruthlessly tears away all the delicacies of tissue that enclose it. Wagner himself, however much he might theorize about poetry, was never a poet; he was simply a versifier who wrote words for music, words sometimes admirably adapted for this purpose, sometimes exceedingly ill-adapted."

So much for the psychological impasse between musician and poet. But there is another psychological knot that involves the auditor. Nietzsche has stated the conditions of this second paradox in "Selected Aphorisms" under the subtitle, "Contradictions in the Idea of Musical Drama": "Music is the language of the commentator, who talks the whole of the time and gives us no breathing space. Moreover his is a difficult language which also requires to be explained. He who step by step has mastered, first the libretto (language!), then converted it into action in his mind's eye, then sought out and understood, and become familiar with the musical symbolism thereto: aye, and has fallen in love with all three things; such a man then experiences a great joy. But how exacting! It is quite impossible to do this save for a few short moments,—such tenfold attention on the part of one's eyes, ears, understanding, and feeling, such acute activity in apprehending without any productive reaction, is far too exhausting!—Only the very fewest behave in this way: how is it then that so many are affected? Because most people are only intermittingly attentive, and are inattentive for sometimes whole passages at a stretch; because they bestow their undivided attention now upon the music, later upon the drama, and anon upon the scenery—that is to say they take the work to pieces.—But in this way the kind of work we are discussing is condemned: not the drama but a moment of it is the result, an arbitrary selection. The creator of a new genre should consider this! The arts should not always be dished up together,—but we should imitate the moderation of the ancients which is truer to human nature."

Admitting the plausibility of Nietzsche's argument and the fact that it has an unfortunate frequency in application, no one who believes in the ceaseless development of the power of the creative artist and of the receptive listener can accept this argument as a final analysis. The whole future of the human mind is here at stake and I, for one, do not admit such narrow boundaries. Nietzsche's protest, in the first place, is the cry of the modern man with super-sensitive nerves: "Tell me one thing at a time!" It is akin to Poe's arbitrary dictum that a hundred lines is the outside limit for sustaining the mood of a lyric poem. Another case of nerves. It is unfortunately true that the strain of our modern industrial existence breeds such cases, even more frequently among listeners than among creative artists. When I see those around me grow restless at a play or a concert that exceeds the normal length, when I become fidgety myself, my mind invariably recalls the contrasting picture of thousands of Japanese men and women, seated on knee and heel, who endure for eight hours through a cycle of four plays, each as long as one of ours. The Orient knows the secret of rapt attention, the antidote to nerves. And if, in the interchange of ideas and of psychology's secrets in a fluid world, we do not assimilate directly from the Orient its stoical self-control, perhaps, as soon as machinery has conquered our world and we have conquered machinery, we shall rediscover the secret which our own race once knew.

A second fault that may be found with Nietzsche's argument is that it sets peremptory limits to the creative artist. Just because no one since the Greeks has fused music, drama. the plastic human body and a plastic physical background into a single work of art that commands effortless, intense and unflagging attention, is no reason why someone may not do it again if we leave the door open and provide sufficient encouragement. As Kenneth Macgowan said in "The Theatre of Tomorrow": "There were once, you know, the Greeks," implying, with a hope that may be vain but is not cringing, the possibility of their reincarnation.

A hasty glance over the efforts to solve the problem through the channel of opera takes us back to Monteverdi and the Florentines who flourished while Shakespeare yet lived. Their misunderstanding of the deeper psychology of the Greek theatre and their preoccupation with its externals are millstones which have hung round the neck of opera ever since. In effect, their attempt to revive the Greek theatre delivered this new genre, bound hand and foot, over to the musician, to the composer, whether he had ever been inside a theatre or not. The successive revolutions of Gluck, Mozart and Weber were superficial. They were concerned with improving the lot of the composer, not with getting down to the psychological roots of the issue.

With his usual clarity of perception, although he had scant success himself at Weimar in his efforts to solve the problem, Goethe pointed out the essential and perennial weakness of the composer as lord of the opera: "A poet who writes for the stage must have a knowledge of the stage, that he may weigh the means at his command, and know generally what is to be done, and what is to be left alone; the opera-composer, in like manner, should have some insight into poetry, that he may know how to distinguish the bad from the good, and not apply his art to something impracticable.

"Carl Maria von Weber should not have composed 'Euryanthe.' He should have seen at once that this was bad material, of which nothing could be made. So much insight we have a right to expect of every composer, as belonging to his art."

A voice crying in the wilderness was that of Ignaz Franz Mosel, who published "Attempt at an Æsthetic of the Musical Drama" in 1813, the year of Wagner's birth. "Much in this book," says Newman, "might have been written by Gluck; some of it might even have been written by Wagner himself. . . . For Mosel the ideal opera is a combination, on practically equal terms, of poetry, music, acting, singing and the art of the stage; the plastic arts, however, play a smaller part in his theory than they do in Wagner's." His idea of a proper text is one that is "thoroughly musical, that is, not only containing nothing that is outside the possibility of musical expression, but also nothing to which music can not give a heightened beauty and a strengthened effect."

If it had not been for Wagner, however, who not only repeated and extended Mosel's theories but put them into brilliant practice, the effort to reincarnate the spirit of the Greek theatre through the channel of opera and music drama would have progressed little beyond the feeble pioneer ventures of Monteverdi. Apologists and opponents of the great German will agree with Newman at least on this broad generalization: "And if there has never been a brain in music that saw so deeply into the springs of character, there has never been a musical brain with such a grasp of a drama as a whole. It was the mighty, tireless synthetic engine that we meet with only some score of times, perhaps, in the whole history of human thought,—in two or three great military commanders, a few great architects, and half-a-dozen philosophers."

A few short paragraphs devoted to the stupendous contribution of this one brain, this one "synthetic engine," to the history of the Synthetic Theatre are scant recognition of his service to the cause, a service which no one who comes after can honestly belittle, no matter how he seeks to profit by Wagner's mistakes. A few lines, however, about the secret springs of Wagner's vision and a few more devoted to the probable causes for the failure of that vision to attain complete realization, are all that can be spared here.

As early as the age of thirty-six, Wagner perceived in

"Art and Revolution" that "with the Greeks the perfect work of art, the drama, was the sum and substance of all that could be expressed in the Greek nature; it was—in intimate connection with its history—the nation itself that stood facing itself in the art-work, that became conscious of itself, and, during a few hours, rapturously devoured, as it were, its own essence." And in the same year, in "The Art-Work of the Future," he predicts, in the flush of his social-revolutionary enthusiasm: "The great united art-work, that must embrace all the genres of art and in some degree undo each of them in order to use it as a means to an end, to annul it in order to attain the common aim of *all,* namely, the unconditioned, immediate representation of perfected human nature,—this great united art-work we can not recognize as the arbitrary need of the individual, but only as the inevitable associated work of the humanity of the future."

Dance, Tone, Poetry—these are the three chief arts which Wagner summons to a mutual sacrifice. How far he succeeded in persuading them to humble themselves for the sake of a nobler goal is witnessed by an amazing repertory of music dramas, performed today on scores of stages more frequently than in his lifetime, and by shelves full of volumes of discussion and appreciation in every language on the globe. Added tribute here would be gratuitous. Perhaps, however, a few words as to why Wagner did not fully achieve his own dream for music drama, for the Synthetic Theatre, may help to illuminate the difficulty of creating such a theatre. Waiving the fact that his social and political ideas often tainted his art with propaganda, let us concentrate on the inner and more vital problem of musician vs.

[146]

poet. I know no more impartial and generally accepted judge than Ernest Newman, and therefore I take the liberty of constructing from his "Wagner as Man and Artist" an analysis of this salient paradox:

"It must always be borne in mind that Wagner's theory of a unification of all the arts in the one art-work was the product of a brain that had comparatively little sympathy with, or understanding of, any art but music. . . .

"That the musician in Wagner ruled the poet is plain enough to us now, but the perception of this truth was always denied to Wagner himself. In 'A Communication to My Friends,' that elucidates so gratefully for us so many dark passages in 'Opera and Drama,' he is persistently blind to the fact that is obvious enough to everyone else. As far as 'Rienzi,' he tells us, he has taken his operatic subjects from ready-made stories, while with 'The Flying Dutchman' he struck out a new path, framing his own libretto out of the simple unpolished outlines of a folk-saga. 'Henceforward,' he goes on to say, 'with regard to all my dramatic works I was in the first instance *Poet,* and only in the complete working-out of the poem did I become once more *Musician.* Only,' he rather naïvely continues, '*I was a poet who was conscious in advance of the power of musical expression for the working out of his poems.*' Quite so: when a subject took possession of him he would see it all in terms of musical expression and development; and unconsciously the poem would be so planned as to provide the needful framework, and no more, for the musical emotion. Later on, after arguing that music is the emotional expression *per se,* but that it can only ally itself with words that con-

[147]

tain the possibility of emotion, he once more lets us see that it was the musician in him that determined his choice of subject and the manner of its treatment. 'What I perceived, I now looked at solely with the eyes of Music; though not,' he rightly points out, '*that* music that was complete within me, and in which I could express myself as in a mother tongue.' Granting that the musical world from the center of which he wished to pour himself out upon poetry was not that of the stereotyped operatic composer, the fact remains that it was from the center of music itself that the outpouring was to come. And we may further grant that 'it was precisely by the facility of musical expression' he had acquired that 'he became a poet.' "

The titanic figure of Wagner, flaws or no flaws, has stood for years like an impregnable fortress, an unscalable mountain peak, to awe other seekers after the Synthetic Theatre into silence or abject and unsuccessful imitation or to turn them ill-naturedly and vainly into the barren field of realistic opera. Only recently have composers mustered the courage and commanded the fresh vision to experiment along wholly original lines in the hope that they will lead by another route to the same goal. Notable among these few have been Malipiero in such works as "Sette-Canzoni," Debussy in "Pelléas et Mélisande," and Schoenberg in "Die Glückliche Hand."

As with opera, an attempt to trace in detail the projected reincarnation of the Synthetic Theatre of the Greeks through the medium of the ballet would lead us into prolonged discussion. That the originators of the classic ballet had any such ambitious aims may be doubted. The vision of Mihail Mordkin, however, touched into life twenty years ago by the flame that was Isadora Duncan and capitalized and institutionalized in the company and repertory of Sergei Diagileff, consciously strove to attain the goal of music drama without words.

The true place of the plastic human body in the Synthetic Theatre—a means, not the end, as in ballet—and Mordkin's continuing service in this broader cause have had the following appraisal by H. I. Brock in *The New York Times:*

"Any authentic style of acting must be based on a perfect command of the instrument—that is, of the actor's own body. And it implies the training of the actor's brain to a use of that bodily command at once intelligent and spontaneous. For such training we have to go to the dancing master. This time it is the dancing master of the pantomime ballet, who has learned to achieve without words, by the mere skillful use of the body, most of the effects that the actor gets with all the arts of speech.

"Already that sort of thing has been done by the Russians, who have gone furthest in developing the ballet as a form of drama. They have not stopped there. They have sent their actors of the spoken word to ballet school and taught them, literally, how to act by teaching them how to dance. The Moscow Art Theatre direction had Mihail Mordkin teaching players what every actor ought to know before the situation created by the Reds drove the great dancer out of the Soviet capital to exile, and almost starvation, in his native Georgia.

"The indirect result is that Mordkin, who has been known in this country chiefly as the partner of Pavlova in her earlier appearances among us, but who has never ceased in his career to be a teacher of dancing and a creator of dances, is now actually engaged in teaching American actors what he used to teach the Russians.

"That thing is rhythm, which can not be got as an act of execution without complete command of the body and entire subservience of that command to the imagination. Mordkin makes drama and poetry of physical exercises and his own motions are the plastic expression of that drama and of that poetry. In a way it is all dancing; in another way it is all acting. Whichever way you take it it is all rhythm. Dancing, says Mordkin, is not an art of the feet. It is an act of the imagination—of the head and heart. And as dancing, in Mordkin's sense, is dramatic expression by means of all the body, it may just as well be called acting."

It seems clear, therefore, that if the world is to know once more the intense exaltation of the Greek Theatre, a realization of the dream of a Synthetic Theatre, then the impelling force, the creative and directing vision, must come from within the theatre, not from the realm of music, literature or any other of the theatre's allied and associated arts and crafts. Gordon Craig foresaw and stated this axiom twenty years ago in his first booklet, "The Art of the Theatre," where he wrote:

"The Art of the Theatre is neither acting nor the play, it is not scene nor dance, but it consists of all the elements of which these things are composed: action, which is the very spirit of acting; words, which are the body of the play; line and color, which are the very heart of the scene; rhythm, which is the very essence of dance. . . . The Art of the Theatre is divided up into so many crafts: acting, scene, costume, lighting, carpentering, singing, dancing, etc., that it must be realized at the commencement that ENTIRE, not PART, reform is needed; and it must be realized that *one* part, one craft, has a *direct* bearing upon each of the other crafts in the theatre, and that no result can come from fitful, uneven reform, but only from a systematic progression. Therefore, the reform of the Art of the Theatre is possible to those men alone who have studied and practiced all the crafts of the theatre."

That Nemirovitch-Dantchenko is this long-awaited artist from within the theatre's ranks who is called by destiny to lead it back by the synchronous practice of its various crafts to its long-lost heritage, that the Moscow Art Theatre Musical Studio is the true modern prototype of the Synthetic Theatre—these are claims that can not be proved and should not be made for a long time to come. This much alone is certain: the Synthetic Theatre will come, not through a great poet or a great composer or a great dancer, or a great artist-designer, but through a "man of the theatre," trained as Nemirovitch-Dantchenko has been trained, and through an institution with a background no less rich in experience and tradition than the Moscow Art Theatre and its Musical Studio. It may be prophetic that the great German and the great Russian were similarly inspired. Richard Wagner was fired to his career as much by the concurrent perfection of the arts of acting and singing in Wilhelmine Schröder-Devrient as he was by the symphonies of Beethoven. And Nemirovitch-Dantchenko became conscious of his dream through the same gigantic and equally-balanced talents in another great actor-singer, Fyodor Chaliapin.

CHAPTER XII

THE HANDWRITING ON THE WALL

THE latest attempt to embody the age-old dream of the Synthetic Theatre has only five winters to its credit. Nevertheless, the Musical Studio of the Art Theatre is looked upon in Moscow already as a Vesuvius within the citadel. No one can tell when it is going to burst forth and bury alive some outworn tradition. The tradition usually passes unmourned. The spectacle of the eruption itself is most exhilarating. And nothing, as we know, provides so fertile a soil for a new growth as the slopes of a volcano. When we remember that the Russian lyric stage, before the birth of the Musical Studio, was more virile and significant than ours, we can estimate roughly what the coming of this company may do to our own doubly outworn traditions in opera and music drama.

The vital principle which has given this company the power to overturn long-established traditions is, as we have seen, Nemirovitch-Dantchenko's determination to develop every element of the lyric stage to its utmost limit. A fine orchestra. That goes without saying. Excellent singers, chosen for their voices, not for their names. Highly gifted actors. Actors who can sing. Singers who can act. Not a competitor of the famous grand opera companies of the world, but a dangerous omen to them, just the same. Stage settings built to interpret the dream of poet and composer, not to make economical use of something already in the storehouse or to provide a stage designer's holiday. Dancers who dance when the action demands choreographic or plastic expression, who endow their every movement with the trained dancer's bodily control, not a troupe of outsiders whom the ballet master drags in whenever he yearns to show how clever he is. And the whole production conceived, rehearsed and presented under the eye of an exacting regisseur as a gripping, thrilling and unified work of art. If the Dramatic Company of the Moscow Art Theatre orchestrated its acting, the Musical Studio goes a step farther and orchestrates its acting, its singing, its body plastic, its scenery and its orchestra.

Effective as this coördination of artistic forces has been in revolutionizing Russia's lyric stage, its potential influence on our own is dependent on several variable factors. Nothing can be an omen unless the time and circumstances are ripe for its significance to be comprehended. Points of contact must exist. The handwriting on the wall must be so placed that the banqueters can see it and it must be expressed in symbols they can understand. Are all these considerations at a favorable posture? I think they are.

First of all, the underlying spirit of this new theatre is that of youth, the eager, contagious ambition of talented boys and girls, an ambition made concrete, effective and articulate by the wise and still youthful spirit of the Studio's creative genius. The significance of this for Russia, as I have pointed out, is that the traditions and the soul of the Moscow Art Theatre have been safely planted in the younger

[153]

generation just as Stanislavsky planted them in the Dramatic Studios. For us, of course, the implication of this youthful spirit is that the Musical Studio meets us on our own ground. The forces on our stage, creative and receptive, are the forces of youth, because the forces of our national life are those of youthful ambition.

Another important point of contact is that in all the productions of the Musical Studio, the most important trends of so-called modern art are for the first time made comprehensible to the man on the street as well as to the connoisseur. In fact, the man on the street in Moscow never thinks of its art as being modern. All he feels is that it is fresh, vital, stimulating, interesting, amusing. And the Russian man on the street doesn't differ greatly from his brother over here.

Perhaps even more than on these conspicuous factors I base my assurance that the Musical Studio arrives at a propitious juncture, on the way Nemirovitch-Dantchenko and his player-singers have taken the boredom and the artificiality out of the lyric stage. Countless thousands of us have had the best will in the world to enjoy opera, light and grand. We never could see why some regisseur didn't provide plausible stage direction and teach his singers how to act. For the first time in my life, in the presence of "Carmencita and the Soldier," it seemed perfectly natural to me that these characters should sing their rôles.

Finally, it is probably true that, trained under the same exacting regime as the Dramatic Company of the Moscow Art Theatre and imbued with the same dramatic ideals, the Musical Studio faces among us a far wider potential audience than was accorded the parent company, due to the fact that we are accustomed already to the use of an alien tongue on our lyric stage. The audiences which enjoyed the repertory of Stanislavsky and his players can be assured of similar satisfaction from the company of Nemirovitch-Dantchenko. And thousands of others who shied at the barrier of an unknown language in the spoken drama will be added to their ranks.

The Musical Studio, therefore, is germane to us. It is ready for us and we for it, because its message is expressed in symbols that are obvious and unequivocal. Moreover, the evolutionary path which has evoked the Musical Studio in Moscow has its rough parallel on our own stage. Before we try to read the handwriting on the wall, let us retrace and compare those paths, the better to understand the omen and its applicability to our local conditions. Acting independently of one another and each in its own way, both Russia and America have conceived a new interest in the lyric stage during the last half decade. In this country, as far back as 1921, "Blossom Time" broke ground and paved the way that led directly to the operettas and the light and comic operas of the past season—"The Student Prince," "The Love Song" and the revivals of Gilbert and Sullivan's "Patience," "The Mikado" and "Princess Ida." In Russia, as we have seen, the lyric revival antedated ours by a year. I purposely use the term "lyric" rather than "romantic," as some critics have done, because it is at the same time more exact and more inclusive, both in the case of America and of Russia. Our lyric revival, in fact, despite its apparently romantic character, was immediately a reaction from the

Cinderella romances of our musical comedies just as much as it was a protest against the jazz revues. In Moscow, romance crossed with satire in the early productions of the Musical Studio gave way in "Lysistrata" to satire that was lyric without being in the least romantic and in "Carmencita" to lyric and tragic passion rather than romance.

Of course, I use the term "lyric," as, for instance, in reference to "Lysistrata," not merely in the restricted sense of "musical" but in its larger application as contrasted with the realistic and naturalistic. On these grounds the antithesis exists both in America and in Russia. The lyric revival here is, at least in part, a reflex from the frank and sometimes embarrassingly intimate realism of our spoken drama. The lyric expansion of the Moscow Art Theatre is a tacit admission that realism in Russia, too, has about reached the end of its tether. No one in his right mind is going forthwith to pronounce the funeral oration over the dead body of realism. Playwrights will continue thus to express themselves, audiences to enjoy that expression. But those who are eager for experiment, for novelty, for fresh stimulus, have turned to lyric drama.

I suppose most of them will say they have turned forward, although, if we take a long enough view of the question, we shall find that they have reverted to a by-gone era for their inspiration. These things move in cycles. In this country the lyric renascence may be traced back to its last previous dominance at the time when Gilbert and Sullivan, Offenbach and Lecocq, were new. The fact that our theatre has been until recently a hit-or-miss affair makes it difficult to follow the thread. In Russia, where the art of the theatre is taken more earnestly if not more seriously, where it has been less susceptible to outside influences and where its richer expression throws successive developments into higher relief, it is possible to retrace each step.

Let us follow back a single cycle, noting the several reactions in both countries where we can and remarking the characteristics of each which the present régime has valued highly enough to salvage. The current lyric revival, then, is a reflex from the cubist and futurist era in Russia, from Meyerhold and the Kamerny Theatre, an era that has its counterpart in our jazz age. It is a corrective reflex, utilizing the freer artistic forms developed by the cubists and futurists and makers of jazz, but taming them and putting them to work as a foil, as a means, not as an end.

One step farther back, and we find that the cubists and futurists and other bad boys of so-called "modern art" revolted in their day against the meticulous and sober realism of the Art Theatre's Dramatic Company, of Belasco in our own country. Here, too, as we have discovered, the lyric revival in Russia has rescued whole pages of precept and practice—not alone the traditions of thorough rehearsal and psychological truth in interpretation, but also the Art Theatre's rare sense of illusion. We were deeply impressed by the way Stanislavsky and his players walked the stage as if they were in no way conscious of the presence of an audience. We shall probably be even more startled when we see the Musical Studio achieve the same feat, for our Western lyric stage has always conceded to the singer the dubious and dowdy privilege of flirting with the spectator and periodically shattering all sense of illusion.

Still farther back, of course, was the realistic revolt against the dry bones of a decayed lyric age—the protest of the Moscow Art Theatre against the false and hollow romanticism that had tumbled down hill from the lyric peaks of Tchaikovsky and Musorgsky; the challenge of Belasco to the rabble that had preëmpted the lyric throne-room of Booth and the lyric playground of Gilbert and Sullivan.

And so we complete the cycle. Having completed it, we see that the present lyric renascence is not a blind copy of its prototype, not a mere reversion to the past. From that past it has borrowed the unrestricted sway of the imagination. But en route through the several intervening phases, new truths have been found, worth preserving. Cycle on cycle could be traced back until we reached the lyric glories of the Greek Theatre. Cycles could be charted for other countries than Russia and America. But we have seen enough to realize that these two nations, apparently, are traveling side by side and that Russia with her richer experience can teach us something that we are ready and eager to learn.

In other words, Morris Gest is bringing the Moscow Art Theatre Musical Studio at the psychological moment when it can best reënforce minds and imaginations longing for leadership, just as he brought the Art Theatre's Dramatic Company at a time when our stage most needed exemplification of repertory presentation and ensemble acting and proof of the central position of the actor in the art of the theatre. Today we are feeling our way in the field of light opera; what we need is a glimpse of experts at work, such as the

Musical Studio provides in "The Daughter of Madame Angot" and "La Périchole." Hereafter, revivals of old works will not be accepted so complacently, either by the critics or the public, if the producer blindly copies the original work and fails to revitalize a libretto that was stillborn. New works will be expected to have an idea behind them and unity and intensity in interpretation if they are to be compared favorably to the Russians.

"Lysistrata," in the second place, is a beacon to those esthetic rebels who are vainly floundering in expressionism for a plastic form of dramatic art to oppose to the strongly intrenched forces of the realists. Here is lyric drama, with emphasis on the drama but with the lyric element providing a rhythmic and unrealistic accompaniment and undertone. Here is drama with its feet on the earth and its head in the clouds.

But the omen of the Musical Studio extends beyond these two implications. Through "Carmencita and the Soldier" and the projected "Boris Godunoff," the handwriting on the wall is directed chiefly at our grand opera. Boasting no pretensions to vocal rivalry with the Metropolitan Opera House, and unacquainted as a stranger with its weak points, Nemirovitch-Dantchenko strikes an unerring and shattering blow at the dead wood of that institution. Once more, for the first time since the days of Oscar Hammerstein and through the medium of the Morris Gest whom Hammerstein trained, the Metropolitan will be compelled to take into consideration factors outside its own walls.

It is almost the voice of Nemesis when Oscar Hammerstein II, co-librettist of "Rose-Marie" and grandson of

Oscar the Great, writes, as he did in the *Theatre Magazine* for May, 1925, unconsciously heralding the Russians: "Some day the operetta will be thrust on us too often and we shall seek something else. What will it be? Will it be a return to a lighter vein—or will we become even more serious, more legitimate as to drama and more operatic as to music? Is there a form of musical play tucked away somewhere in the realm of possibilities which could attain the heights of grand opera and still keep sufficiently human to be entertaining?

"I have an extravagant theory that little light opera, a healthy youth all alive and ambitious, can be so developed that he can come in at the back door and give his big brother, grand opera, a stiff battle for artistic honors. Certainly the younger one has a great advantage. He is continually moving and progressing."

That is exactly what has happened in Moscow. The Musical Studio is the little brother. And the big brother, the Great State Theatre after having once refused to assimilate Nemirovitch-Dantchenko and his ideas, is now vainly trying to copy him. And the copy is—a copy; better, probably, than the lifeless stencils that preceded it, but manifestly an imitation based on an unsure footing.

The Metropolitan can, of course, ignore the Russians. But its patrons, finding life and exhilaration in the Russians instead of schematism, will ask embarrassing questions. And no attempt to meet those questions can succeed by imitation, by slight adjustments, by a cursory housecleaning. Moscow's Great State Theatre has proved that. The Metropolitan or any American institution which seeks to do for us

what the Russians have done for the world will have to feel
and build its own way, based solely on the fundamental
premise of the actor-singer, the singing actor. Unfortunately, we have no Moscow Art Theatre on which to draw
for spiritual and technical guidance. But that should not
discourage us. Considering our lack of tools, the challenge
is all the greater, for if we achieve, the more will be the
credit. Both for those who are complacent and for those
who despair, I can not forbear quoting once more, as I did
in "The Russian Theatre" those spurring and heartening
words of Otto H. Kahn in "Some Observations of Art in
America":

"If, as I trust and believe will come to pass, we will give
to art that full scope and place and honor to which it is
entitled, if we make it widely and easily accessible to the
people, if we afford serious encouragement, fostering attention and adequate opportunity to genuine aspirations and
talent, and due reward to genuine merit, we shall, I am convinced, astonish the world and ourselves by the greatness
and intensity of the manifestation of the American spirit
in art."

CHAPTER XIII

THE FIRST STUDIO GROWS UP

ON the evening of December 7, 1924, the Moscow Art Theatre, Second, celebrated the tenth anniversary and the five hundred and sixty-first performance of its production of Dickens' "The Cricket on the Hearth." That is not quite an exact statement, to be sure, for it was the First Studio that created this deathless little "Rip Van Winkle" of the modern Russian stage back in the days when the war was young. The First Studio was young, too, having to its credit only an experimental production of Heijermans' "The Loss of 'The Hope,'" and "The Cricket" established the modest little group of players in a secure place on Moscow's theatrical hearthstone. Still, though this cozy little comedy belongs to the tender youth of that populous, ambitious and all but independent new playhouse in Theatre Square which calls itself the Moscow Art Theatre, Second, the very fact that it is fondly retained in the repertory is proof of the continuing identity of the First Studio under its aspiring new title. And if this be not proof enough, consider how four members of the original cast were still playing at the tenth jubilee—Maria Durasova as Mary Peerybingle, Nadiezhda Bromley as Mistress Fielding, Vera Solovyova as Bertha, and Boris Sushkievitch as Caleb Plummer.

Just as surely as the Musical Studio is the product of the creative genius of Nemirovitch-Dantchenko, so the First Studio grown up is beholden to the vision of Stanislavsky. Of course, although each of these children has been the particular protégé of one of the parents, both of them have profited by the environment and the traditions which the parents built jointly into the Moscow Art Theatre itself. After treading a common path for two decades, more or less, the founders of the Art Theatre conceived of two different channels for perpetuating the spirit of that theatre. That is all.

The circumstances of the upbringing of these two children, however, render one of them, Stanislavsky's, the more interesting from the standpoint of institutional development if not yet on the score of original achievement. Continuing the analogy of the family Mhat, which I quoted from the amusing pen of Tchernoyaroff in Chapter III, the Musical Studio was reared with little if any domestic responsibility. True, it was born of the need for keeping the home stage busy and it has shared in that task ever since birth. But it was never asked to fetch and carry for the elders. It was not expected to train recruits for the Dramatic Company. Without being pampered or spoiled, it has had free rein for self-development, for the pursuit of its own career.

Not so the First Studio. It was founded by Stanislavsky not only to enable him to apply his "system" of instruction to unspoiled youth but also to drill new levies for the main company more effectively than a school could do. In Chapter LVI of "My Life in Art" he admits the latter purpose thus: "I had dreamed that the actor who grew up in

[163]

the Studio would make his first timid artistic steps in a small room which was built so as not to violate the inner creative life of the beginning artist. . . . Only after all the artistic qualities of the Studio pupil were strengthened and it would be easy for him to carry his rôle to a large stage, would he be taken by us into the family of the older actors of the Theatre proper, into the midst of the true preservers of the traditions of Russian art."

That was a perfectly rational fatherly ambition. Many a family fortune, many a business enterprise, even professional reputations, have been handed on from generation to generation on this principle. On the other hand, many a happy home has been hopelessly, and needlessly, shattered by the father's blind insistence on fealty to the family tradition and the son's determination to strike out on a new tangent, to make his own way in his own way. Stanislavsky had neither the luck to achieve his first ambition nor the misfortune of an obstinate temper. When the Studio began to assert its independence, he stood ready to give guidance and counsel. With some philosophy, more misgivings and even more solicitude, he analyzed his refractory offspring thus:

"Perhaps because the desired *rapprochement* between the Theatre and the Studio could not take place, the actors who grew up in the Studio preferred to remain the first in a village rather than to become the second in Rome. In the Studio they soon became famous. But when they came to us in the Theatre they were only ordinary actors in our group. God knows what such a phenomenon threatened! Perhaps the Studios, demanding so little of themselves, would become good little theatres with small desires which they would be able to fulfill beautifully. Could such little theatres serve the Eternal in art, which must always make tremendous demands on the artist, demands that are always higher than his abilities? Or perhaps these little theatres would be satisfied with fashionable, speedy and cheap success, which this sphere of our art always yields."

For ten years, Stanislavsky's philosophy was necessary; his misgivings and his solicitude, plausible. The First Studio, particularly, lived on the reputation of its "Cricket," its "Twelfth Night," its "Eric XIV." True, it removed to larger quarters. But, conversely, it lost Baklanova to the Musical Studio, Vakhtangoff to the Third Studio and then to death, Kolin to Balieff abroad and later to oblivion.

But young Tchehoff remained. And suddenly, without warning—just as a young man finds himself, quits floundering and starts off under full steam toward a definite goal—the First Studio came of age a year ago and grew up over night around the nucleus of this gifted nephew of the beloved playwright. Under the stimulus of the Art Theatre's reorganization, imparting its own stimulus to that reordering of the household, the First Studio ceased to be the youthful and indifferent Misha; became the dignified, mature and ambitious Mihail Constantinovitch; rented the spacious and imposing Nezlobin or Novy Theatre, facing and flanking the century-old playhouses supported by the State in Theatre Square; assumed, with parental permission, the prerogatives and responsibilities of the Moscow Art Theatre, Second; and boldly announced a "modern" production of "Hamlet."

[165]

The executive and administrative structure required by this program has been sufficiently indicated in the chart accompanying Chapter III. Every function of the theatre, as I have said, is beholden directly to Tchehoff through a board of directors over which he presides. He is answerable, in turn, only to Nemirovitch-Dantchenko by the loose thread that binds monarch and father-confessor. His rôle, therefore, is not unlike that of the two founders of the Art Theatre in its early days, and, like them, he has round him a faithful band of co-workers, trained to play together by years of intimate association. Including Tchehoff himself, I count an even dozen artists in the theatre's first line today who were the backbone of the First Studio ensemble back in the winter of 1917-18: Ivan Bersenieff, Boris Sushkievitch, Valentin Smuishlyaieff, Alexi Tcheban, V. Gotovtseff, A. Geyrot, and Mlles. Vera Solovyova, Sophia Ghiatsintova, Maria Durasova, S. Birman and Nadiezhda Bromley.

At first glance, it seems that the Moscow Art Theatre, Second, has chosen to stress its likeness, its family resemblance, to its parent, rather than its independent personality. Simple, severe seats duplicating those of the original Art Theatre were installed when the débris of various tenants since the Revolution was cleared out of the building. The insignia of the Sea-Gull enters into the decorative scheme, reposes on the curtain. The ushers wear identical uniforms. The house is kept as scrupulously spotless. The program carries the same warning: "During the performance, entrance into the auditorium is prohibited." Applause is frowned on until the final curtain falls. The prompter is never heard, as he is in all other Moscow playhouses except the Art Theatre—constant rehearsals see to that! The repertory is billed with that of the parent. The parent pays a visit in full force to the stage of the son once or twice a week with "The Lower Depths" or another play in the current repertory. And in return for this courtesy, young Tchehoff not only retains his formal membership in the parent company but joins it on occasion to play the rôle of Hlestyakoff in "The Inspector General."

Now, lest these similarities may have misled you, pick up a program of the Moscow Art Theatre, Second. First, you will note that it is illustrated with the leading figures in the play; next, that the regisseurs have provided an explanation of their interpretation of the play; and finally, that everyone who had a hand in the production is duly credited— not only the players but the regisseurs, their assistant, the scenic artist, the composer, the director of the chorus, the master of fencing, the makers of the costumes, the hats, the wigs, the coiffures and the stage settings, the head of the mechanical staff, the stage manager and the electrician! In the Art Theatre, these details have always been discreetly veiled behind the impersonal visage of the theatre itself. But youth and independence demand recognition.

Further evidence of these forces and of a spirit not unlike that of the Musical Studio in its disparagement of the strictly realistic tenets of the parent emerges in the regisseurs' apology for their work. Let us read what they have to say about their "Hamlet" while we wait for the curtains to part:

"What interested us in Shakespeare's 'Hamlet' is the

juxtaposition of two types of human nature and the development between them of the struggle with each other. One of them is of a protesting nature, heroic, fighting for the affirmation of that which forms the substance of his life. This is our Hamlet. In order to bring out more vividly and to underscore his supreme significance, we had to cut the text of the tragedy and eliminate from it everything that might impede its whirlwind impetuosity. To this end we consciously infringed upon an age-old tragedy for the sake of a better understanding of Hamlet himself. As early as the middle of the second act, he takes his sword in hand and never relinquishes it until the end of the tragedy. We have emphasized the restlessness of Hamlet by condensing the obstacles which he met on his way. From this point emerges the motive of King and eternity. King Claudius embodies all that which impedes the heroic Hamlet. He is egoistic, conservative, haughty and pompous. He is a hindrance to everything that moves forward. And our Hamlet holds firm in the elemental and sacred struggle against all that the King represents. Based on the understanding of Hamlet and the King as two forces constantly struggling with each other, the entire cast of characters is grouped in two hostile camps, confronting one another. One of them, with Hamlet against the King, includes Horatio, Marcellus, Bernardo, Francisco, all the Players and also Hamlet's beloved Ophelia. The other camp, with the King against Hamlet, consists of all the Courtiers, headed by Polonius. And finally, there are those characters whose relation to the tragedy seems to place them in the hands of both fighting camps, for example Laertes and the Queen.

"In order to concentrate our color values, we deemed it necessary to transfer the action of 'Hamlet' to the Middle Ages, as to an epoch which expressed with dazzling brightness the elements and the spirit of this struggle—that is, the heroic and the opponent of the heroic.

"Hence we derived the elements of Gothic architecture, the medieval costume and the medieval painting, which became the basis of the external aspects of the production. Hence we derived the pomp of the court scenes in accordance with the brilliance and splendor with which the Middle Ages surrounded the sovereign of its world. Still, under no circumstances do we wish to solve the tragedy in an every-day realistic manner. Therefore, we disclose the Middle Ages as our creative fancy has dictated. We take from the Middle Ages only that which emphasizes more sharply the basic lines of the struggle between two ancient adverse elements: the heroic and the bright; the conservative and the dark."

Obviously, the "Hamlet" which the regisseurs, Smuishlyaieff, Tatarinoff and Tcheban, have devised will not be an Elizabethan revival, a clutter of realistic walls and armor, a Sweet Prince in dress suit, or a Gordon Craig pageant in white and gold against changing screens, such as the Art Theatre itself disclosed with Katchaloff as Hamlet a dozen years ago. This surmise proves correct when the Sea-Gull curtains part. Instead, we have a "Hamlet" seen through colored and distorted lenses, a "Hamlet" startlingly stylized. If I were to characterize it briefly, I would say that it is the Jones-Hopkins-Barrymore "Hamlet" carried from the realm of ordered fantasy into a world of exaggerated nightmare.

[169]

There are steps. But they don't stay put; they shift here and there for the various scenes. The Ghost, likewise, is a shaft of light, though its lines are uttered by Hamlet's subconscious self. Probably the paragraph from their apology which Tchehoff's regisseurs have executed most successfully is that which calls for sharp contrast in the aspect and the mien of the hostile camps. Not only in costume and bearing and control of stage lighting is this antithesis conveyed, but also in a subtle atmosphere which the players radiate from their inner consciousness. One group distinctly attracts; the other just as intensely repels. The means intended to propagate revulsion against the Court are particularly expressive —degenerate facial masks, mincing gait, hollow, artificial and insincere voice tones, servility alternating with insolence. Hamlet and his camp are not so vividly etched; they appear for what they are rather by contrast. As a whole, therefore, the production stands somewhere between the Art Theatre's traditional realism and the purely cerebral constructivism of Tairoff and Meyerhold—probably nearer the latter than the former. It is amusing to see how bigoted critics of the new dispensation snatch the radical interpretation of the tragedy and particularly the discredit which Tchehoff and his fellow-artists leap upon royalty, to make of "Hamlet" a proletarian holiday!

Although Tchehoff's Hamlet has made him Moscow's darling today, I was distinctly disappointed in his performance. His unmistakable talents, I feel sure, are not those which Hamlet demands. And in striving to make them fit the task, he strains and tears his voice, much as John Barrymore did on his off nights or when he was consciously try-

[170]

ing to make a good impression. In both cases, Russian and American, half the effort wisely applied would achieve twice the results. In the graveyard scene Tchehoff was particularly fine and moving. His Hamlet was still young when I saw it, and if he will take this finely and sensitively poised scene as his keynote, he will ultimately become a great Hamlet. But Moscow, as I have said, thinks he is one already and bestows such plaudits as even Katchaloff never won for his Prince of Denmark.

In addition to "Hamlet" and the older plays of First Studio days, the current repertory includes Lieskoff's "The Spendthrift," Tolstoy's "Love—the Golden Book," an inept performance of "King Lear," and "The Taming of the Shrew.' In rehearsal, if not already presented to the public, are: "Petersburg," by Alexander Bieley, and "The Flea," a comedy by Eugene Zamiatin, written on the theme of a novel by Lieskoff entitled "Left-handed." Zamiatin is the author of the satiric novel, "We," which was published in this country last winter but has not yet appeared in Russia. For his play, the celebrated artist, Kruimoff, has designed the settings.

From this survey of the Moscow Art Theatre, Second, it is apparent that if Stanislavsky's first hopes for the First Studio were not realized, neither have his forebodings come true. Content for a while to be "a good little theatre with small desires which it would be able to fulfill beautifully," the First Studio has felt the urge of high ambition. Its true career still lies ahead. But so did that of the Art Theatre itself back in 1898. And the people who founded it were little if any younger than Tchehoff and his co-workers.

[171]

Already the ambition of the Moscow Art Theatre, Second, visualizes for it a tour abroad and an audience waiting for it in America. Perhaps—in time. But not yet. "Hamlet," "Erik XIV," "Twelfth Night" and "The Cricket on the Hearth" are all good reserve productions, but what this company needs for success abroad is a series of genuine Russian productions of Russian plays. To expand the repertory in this direction will take time. In the last seven years, the map of the Theatre International has shifted its boundaries. When I returned from Moscow in 1918, I hadn't the faintest dream that the parent company of the Art Theatre would ever budge from the old homestead, though a visit from the First Studio seemed a desirable possibility. Today, the veterans have come and gone, leaving behind them standards that the Studios, even grown up, will find staring them in the face to challenge them even more severely than they do at home.

MIHAIL TCHEHOFF

Nephew of the Playwright and of Olga Knipper-Tchehova and Director and Outstanding Genius of the Moscow Art Theatre, Second

A Life Portrait Made a Week Before His Departure from America

In One of His Greatest Rôles, Satine, in Gorky's "The Lower Depths"

CONSTANTIN SERGEIEVITCH STANISLAVSKY

CHAPTER XIV

Precept and Practice

Few events in the Russian capital illustrate so vividly the breakneck pace of Revolution as the consolidation into a single Dramatic Studio and School of the several Studios of the Moscow Art Theatre outside the First, at the time of the general reorganization a year ago. Born one after another within a few brief years to meet irreconcilable demands, they have run their course on their separate paths and have suddenly discovered that they have more in common than they have at odds. Like pioneers dashing off into the wilderness for complete independence, they have come to a realization that there is something more important than mere freedom—mutual welfare and the give-and-take of coöperation.

Stanislavsky has vividly recounted the natal history of these Studios in Chapter LVI of his autobiography: "The generation of the First Revolution (1905) seemed to be altogether different people than we were. If we advance a little in point of time, we see that the following generation was just as sharply differentiated from the generation of the First Studio as they were differentiated from us. This new generation went even further in the sense of freedom, in the weakening of discipline, in the strengthening of independence,—they knew the years of the war. After them

[173]

came still another generation brought up amidst the thunder of cannon, the insidiousness of poison gases, bombs, catastrophes, world perturbations, Biblical hunger, all sorts of cares and national poverty, which history will remember with horror. All these generations that grew up before our eyes do not understand each other well. This was one of the reasons why one Studio after another came to life around our Theatre. These Studios were born because one generation could not fuse with another. Time will show what the result of this will be, whether the art whose principles were always the same will perish, or whether it will grow richer by the discoveries of new technical methods and the researches in the sphere of outward form."

What seems to have happened in Moscow, so swiftly that the time Stanislavsky mentions as solvent agent dwindles to a mere moment, is this: Just as Stanislavsky himself discovered, in the middle years of the Art Theatre when he abandoned tradition and realism and went roaming after the strange gods of experiment in outward form, there is something more important, more vital, more enduring, in the theatre than its visual aspect, its scenery and costumes. This something is the creative power of the actor. It took Stanislavsky years of restless worry and floundering with stage tricks and illusions to realize that, when, for instance, he had hit upon the use of black velvet curtains for uncanny effects in Andreieff's "The Life of Man," the illusion had only a narrow application. The reflex of these years of experiment was the discovery of something more eternal, more universal—his "system" of training the actor's creative power. But life rides on the whirlwind in Moscow today. It took the heterodox Studios less time than it did their godfather to abandon, or rather to put in its place, the inferior good and to unite for the concerted pursuit of their profession's fundamentals.

The reorganization of the Art Theatre's forces, therefore, saw the consolidation of the entire Second Studio with the major portion of the Third Studio into a new Dramatic Studio and School, more closely connected with the parent stage than any of the Studios had been theretofore, while the recalcitrants of the Third Studio and almost the entire Fourth Studio cut loose from the Art Theatre altogether to tarry longer with radical essays in stage externals. It must not be inferred from this, however, that the new Studio has foresworn experiment in outward form. The birth of the several Studios, with this very end in view in one phase or another, had Stanislavsky's blessing alongside his solicitude lest the greater good be swamped by the lesser. But the lesson of proportionate values has been learned in the only school worth attending—experience.

What is this greater good which Stanislavsky hopes by his "system" to achieve, which he has been chosen to inculcate and develop as adviser to the new Studio and School? Ever since Gordon Craig came back to the Western World from Moscow, we have heard about this "system." Thirteen years have passed, books have been written about it, Studio after Studio was formed for the purpose of applying it, Stanislavsky himself and at least the younger and more pliable members of the Art Theatre's Dramatic Company have exhibited its results before our eyes, its author has devoted to it whole chapters of his autobiography. And yet

[175]

it is not much clearer to us than it was when we first heard of it.

The best verbal formulation of this "system" yet available may be found in certain paragraphs of Chapter XLVIII of "My Life in Art." Stanislavsky thus puts question and answer:

" 'Are there no technical means for the creation of the creative mood, so that inspiration may appear oftener than is its wont?' This does not mean that I was going to create inspiration by artificial means. That would be impossible. What I wanted to learn was how to create a favorable condition for the appearance of inspiration by means of the will, that condition in the presence of which inspiration was most likely to descend into the actor's soul. . . .

"But how was one to make this condition no longer a matter of mere accident, to create it at the will and order of the actor?

"If it is impossible to own it at once, then one must put it together bit by bit, using various elements for its construction. If it is necessary to develop each of the component elements in one's self separately, systematically, by a series of certain exercises—let it be so! . . . Of course the ordinary, simply able man will never become a genius, but it will help him to approach and in time to become like the genius, of one school with the genius, the servant of the same art as the genius. But how was one to reach the nature and the component elements of the creative mood?"

After recounting discouragements and failures, Stanislavsky continues: "I came to understand that creativeness begins from that moment when in the soul and imagination of the actor there appears the magical, creative *if*. While only actual reality exists, only practical truth which a man naturally can not but believe, creativeness has not yet begun. Then the creative *if* appears, that is, the imagined truth which the actor can believe as sincerely and with greater enthusiasms than he believes practical truth, just as the child believes in the existence of its doll and of all life in it and around it. From the moment of the appearance of *if,* the actor passes from the plane of actual reality into the plane of another life, created and imagined by himself. Believing in this life, the actor can begin to create."

How to make the *if* appear in really potent form, is another problem and one to which Stanislavsky has given his best mind and time for a dozen years. Like a scientist in his laboratory, he has been intent upon gathering all the data, investigating all the phenomena, rather than upon drawing premature conclusions from his data or upon devising a temporary theory to account for the phenomena. It is for that reason that he has steadfastly refused to put his "system" into words. It is for that reason that he writes in his autobiography: "My system can not be explained in an hour or in a day even. It must be systematically and practically studied for years. It does good only when it becomes the second nature of the actor, when he stops thinking of it consciously, when it begins to appear naturally, as of itself."

In the nature of the case, there can be no brief generalization. Since the problem is so intimately concerned with the unique psychology of the individual actor, there must be hundreds of approaches to the solution, an infinite number of combinations of those approaches. Then, too, in the nature of the case, it would be treacherously easy for the actor to delude himself into thinking that he had absorbed the theory if its author were to attempt a brief generalization. At once, the world of the stage would be flooded with half-equipped "teachers" of the "system," just as the United States today is overrun from coast to coast by self-styled masters of the Imperial Russian Ballet who never got beyond the rear line of the corps in Moscow or Petersburg.

Never before, until the foundation of the new Dramatic Studio and School, has Stanislavsky had a free hand to apply his "system," to bring it to the point where it may be formulated for all time. The older actors of the parent stage were too set in their ways to benefit greatly by it, even if they had the best will in the world to do so. The former Studios grew up to independent maturity faster than their godfather could master his own mind with regard to his "system." Today, however, he feels sufficient assurance in it to keep abreast of his youthful protégés. And meanwhile, in fulfillment of his promise in "My Life in Art," he is slowly preparing the authorized outline of his "system" for publication in a new volume.

Stanislavsky's new charges, both Studio and School, have an identical function to perform with relation to the Art Theatre—the training of actors and stage directors to supplement the present forces of the parent company and to replace them as they retire. They share the same roof, the same stage. And while the Studio is a logical stepping-stone from the School to the Art Theatre, it is not a compulsory way-station. A student as well as a player in the

Studio may be enrolled directly in the Dramatic Company. Nevertheless, they are organized and administered separately, as the chart in Chapter III indicates.

Handmaiden both to elder sister and to parent, the School finds ample opportunity for exacting practice, but, in addition, it has staged from its own ranks and for public presentation a dramatization of Dickens' "The Battle of Life," with other productions in rehearsal. The course of instruction is three years, and the high standards Stanislavsky and his teaching staff maintain are apparent from the fact that only five applicants for admission out of 142 were accepted at a recent examination.

Admission to the Studio, likewise, is by examination or by graduation from the School. Here there are no set courses and no fixed time limit before promotion to the Dramatic Company, for instruction is individual and advancement depends on the ability of the student. For repertory, the Studio is dependent chiefly on Calderon's "The Fairy Lady" and Andreieff's "Youth," with "Yelizaveta Petrovna" in the offing, a play by Dmitry Smolin, poet and adapter of the Musical Studio's version of "Lysistrata." The greatest casualty of the consolidation of the Studios, of course, is the disappearance from the repertory of "Princess Turandot," the brilliant modernist production by which the Third Studio made a name for itself in its first season. "Turandot," however, is not merely a sacrifice to reorganization. Vakhtangoff, its regisseur, died shortly after he had started the Third Studio. And Zovadsky, the Katchaloff of the younger generation of players and "Turandot's" mainstay, has been drafted to the parent stage.

[179]

Regretful as it may be from one angle, the new Dramatic Studio and School seem to me to have a surer opportunity to fulfill the duties expected of them than did the old First Studio. The latter was founded at a time when vacancies in the parent company were few and infrequent. These young people couldn't afford to wait ten to twenty years for their fling. And so they struck out on their own path. Henceforth, even if a hale old age is to be the well-earned lot of the first line players of the Dramatic Company, there will be an increasing number of rôles each season which they will have to abandon to younger artists. If that thought brings a sigh of sorrow, there should be consolation in the fact that the mechanism has been developed whereby that first line, as teachers, can pass on their secret to their inheritors.

CHAPTER XV

A GRAND DUKE INCOGNITO

A DROSHKY rattles up over the cobblestones of the Street of the Moscow Art Theatre, turns into the alleyway to the Art Theatre's courtyard and halts. From it descends a cylindrical bundle of fur topped by a trim Astrahan hat, which forthwith walks off through a private door, ascends a flight of stairs, enters a long dimly-lit room studded with memories of a ripe career, and finally discloses a little man, stockily built, with distinguished mien, and trim as his hat in attire, graying beard and thinning hair. Meeting him here, you know at once who he is; but if you encountered him driving in the Bois or in the smoke-room of a trans-Atlantic liner, you would set him down, as I wrote in "The Russian Theatre," for a grand duke traveling incognito. For Vladimir Ivanovitch Nemirovitch-Dantchenko is the First Gentleman of the contemporary theatre.

He is likewise one of its first artists, certainly one of the five or six foremost living producers or regisseurs. In that connection, probably no living figure of his importance in any of the arts is so thoroughly misapprehended in our Western world. Repute outside Russia makes him responsible for the administrative perfection and executive efficiency of the Art Theatre. To that extent, rumor is right. But when it goes on to limit him to these functions, it is doing him, the Art Theatre and Stanislavsky himself a grave injustice. For, in addition to providing the theatre with business brains and diplomatic acumen, he has contributed uniquely to its literary taste and prestige and largely to its refinement and catholicity of taste. In other words, he and Stanislavsky have shared equally in the artistic burdens of the child of their joint imagination, and they should share equally in the credit for their achievement. Likewise, we should be scrupulously careful and explicit in assigning credit to each for his private projects—to Nemirovitch-Dantchenko for the Musical Studio; to Stanislavsky for the old Dramatic Studios and for his Operatic Studio.

The reasons for our erroneous impression of Nemirovitch-Dantchenko's true function in the Art Theatre are patent. The English-speaking world had its first vivid picture of this institution, first became widely aware of its existence, through the stimulating and enthusiastic pen of Gordon Craig, in the first edition of "On the Art of the Theatre." Now, Craig had most if not all of his personal and official contacts with the Art Theatre through Stanislavsky, whose urging had induced the directors to invite him to Moscow to superintend the production of "Hamlet" and who, owing to his supreme genius in fantasy, had been chosen as one of Craig's assistant regisseurs. Furthermore, Moscow was still ringing with Stanislavsky's triumph with "The Blue Bird." For one of Craig's temperamental and impressionistic powers of observation—an asset as well as a liability—it was quite natural that he should write, "Its director, Constantin Stanislavsky . . . ," wholly ignoring the twin director.

Casual visitors to Moscow repeated and spread the mistake, owing probably to the fact that Stanislavsky as an actor, visible in the flesh, was a handy embodiment of the spirit of the institution. In the propagation of this faulty emphasis, I, too, must confess a hand, for the crisis through which the Art Theatre passed, during the winter I spent in Moscow gathering material for "The Russian Theatre," compelled each of the two directors to limit himself intensively to a single function. To Nemirovitch-Dantchenko naturally fell the pilot's rôle of charting a course that lay through days of sudden and arbitrary governmental decrees, nights of desultory gunfire, weeks when the wood supply threatened to vanish, months when it seemed that the Art Theatre would have to give up the struggle and close its doors. To Stanislavsky fell the decision of all artistic problems. The momentary assignment of rôles, therefore, quite easily, though unfortunately, clouded the long view of permanent functions.

The opportunity and the necessity of repairing this misapprehension presents itself, of course, with the coming of the Musical Studio and Nemirovitch-Dantchenko in person at its head. Nothing less than a survey of his eventful career can accomplish this end, particularly the formative years leading up to the founding of the Moscow Art Theatre.

Born in 1858 in Tiflis in the Caucasus, whither his father, a Government official of moderate means, had migrated from the province of Yekaterinoslav in Little Russia, Vladimir Ivanovitch was caught at an early age by the lure of the theatre. He grew up alone with his toy stage on the broad Russian window sill, a stage that obeyed every dramatic and operatic whim of his eager imagination, for he had little contact with his brothers and his sister. Something there must have been in the blood that had not emerged in his forebears, for the sister, Varvara Ivanovna, became a well-known dramatic and operatic figure, while one of his brothers, Ivan Ivanovitch, became an actor. The eldest brother, Vassily Ivanovitch, on the contrary, elected the profession of letters, was the foremost correspondent at the front in the Russo-Turkish wars, wrote the accredited biography of their hero, General Skobeleff, reported the Russo-Japanese war, wrote a shelf full of novels and is still active at the age of eighty-two in Prague.

Literature all but claimed the younger boy, too. In fact, there was a tussle for twenty years between it and the theatre for possession of his soul. The theatre finally won, but not until Vladimir Ivanovitch had made a name for himself as the ablest playwright and one of the most promising novelists of the epoch that stood between the passing of Ostrovsky, Dostoievsky and Turgenieff and the arrival of Tchehoff and Gorky. School days saw the beginning of the struggle. Alongside labored experiments in the novel, the short story and the dramatic form, the boy seized every opportunity to act on the amateur stage—in Tiflis with the young Sumbatoff, and later in Rostoff, Pyatigorsk and Moscow. While in the University on a scholarship that compelled him to specialize in mathematics, he attracted the attention of the actors, Lyensky and Pravdin; but his dual fate used a strange instrument, for it was Pravdin's introduction to the editor, Alexandroff, which gave him a practical foothold in the literary field. Immediate success as a critic of music and drama and as a story writer, combined with his short stature, assured the young man's ambition for success in letters the upper hand over his longing for the theatre—a place it held for nearly two decades, although the defeated dream found partial expression in the writing of numerous plays.

The periodicals and newspapers of Moscow and Petersburg opened their columns to the young writer—first *The Russian Gazette* and then *The Awakener, Recreation, The Russian Courier, The Moscow Weekly* and others. Literary circles opened their doors to him, in spite of the independence of his criticisms and his determination to fly in the face of contemporary custom in abstaining from political issues in his stories. Doors opened still wider into a world of social culture on his marriage in 1886 to the Baroness Yekaterina Nikolaievna Korf, lifelong companion and adviser. It was probably his abhorrence of propaganda in literature that led him to an early acquaintance with Tchehoff and admiration for his human and politically disinterested style.

The short story, which kept company with the critical *feuilleton* as the young author's favorite literary form through the decade of the '80's, finally gave way to the novel in 1890. "Literary Pensioners," his first long narrative, at once established, without floundering or experiment, the main lines which he was to follow in succeeding works— a genre picture shrewdly observant of contemporary life, posing but not solving the issues of the day and distilling in a gallery of varied portraits the heart-breaking despondency of the epoch. His newspaper connections had revealed to him life at first hand—not only the professional problems of his fellow-writers and artists but the less subjective, more naïve turbulencies of life as it came to crises in the police courts. "Literary Pensioners," therefore, not only lifted the veil on the moral mire of petty journalism and particularly on that type of writer who serves literature for his bread, not for his soul's ease, but it also embodied in concrete form the weak will that ran like a disease through all the professions and all the classes of Russian life of the '80's and '90's.

"Mist" (1892-93) has for its central character a man whose inclination for the theatre might have brought him success if his love of woman had not confused and deadened his reason, his conscience and his will. "Death in Life" (1894) varies the theme of "Literary Pensioners" by presenting a writer of undoubted talent whose warped and dilletante attitude toward life permitted that talent no wholesome expression. "Governmental Inspection" (1895) is the portrait of a provincial official who has enough of an objective sense to discern the absurdity of his being placed in charge of the affairs of life and death of tens of thousands of people as able or abler than himself, but who lacks the will either to resign and give up the farce or to pursue actively his literary ambitions.

The best rounded of his novels thus far, "Governmental Inspection," brought the following tribute from Tchehoff: "In subtlety, in purity of style and in every other sense, this is the best of all your works that I know. The impression is powerful; only the conclusion, beginning with the conversation with the clerk, becomes somewhat giddy, although it should be *piano,* for it is very sad. You have a great knowledge of life, and I repeat (I have said this before) that you are growing better and better all the time, and practically every year you build your talent one story higher."

The next floor in Nemirovitch-Dantchenko's literary structure bore the title "A Drama Behind the Scenes" (1896). Into this story of the tribulations of a group of idealistic young actors who try in vain to make headway against the intolerance, the bigotry and the cheap standards of a small provincial city, the author has crowded all his observations of life behind the stage's curtain, all his own suppressed longing for participation in that life, no matter how difficult it may be. There is something almost prophetic in his instinctive understanding of the obstacles which an earnest band of players must face, for less than two years later, amid the early struggles of the Moscow Art Theatre he was called on to act a major rôle in his own drama behind the scenes.

"On the Steppes" (1897) was Nemirovitch-Dantchenko's valedictory to the novel. These are not the vast, rolling plains of Tchehoff, drowsy under a burning sun. Instead, they are the scene of struggle—speculative struggle among the landed proprietors and the bitter, grinding labor of those who till the soil but do not own it or their lives. Out of the pages of this story, half of which was suppressed by the censor, emerges the conviction that the land belongs to him who works it. In his passionate understanding of Russia's consuming land-hunger, the artist here verges close to propaganda, although he rests content with uttering his conviction

[187]

—he has no program, no panacea, to propose. He is still posing his problem, not solving it.

A survey of the stories of Nemirovitch-Dantchenko yields one outstanding conclusion: In him, the novelist bows respectfully to the dramatist. In the first place, his narrative action is the kind that the imagination can easily visualize. His plots unfold with all the compactness and logical sequence of a good play. Rhythm, tempo, climax—all these are not only as highly developed as in a play, but they are sensitively adapted to the case in hand. At will, he can be premonitory, passionate, calm, as the case warrants and as a dramatist must always be if he is to establish a definite mood for his play. And fianlly, he has the true dramatist's knack for disappearing from the scene of action and for letting his characters speak for themselves. For five and six pages, his conversations run on unimpeded by "he said" or "she replied," thus attaining the intensity usually associated only with the theatre.

If the writing of these novels gave Nemirovitch-Dantchenko a secure literary prestige and a keen sense of literary values to bring as a dowry to the founding of the Art Theatre and to serve as a touchstone in the molding of its repertory through the years, his experience as a playwright not only served the same end but also gave him assurance and authority for supervising the revision and rewriting of the librettos for the repertory of his Musical Studio. Far otherwise was his purpose in becoming a playwright, for he vainly hoped thereby to counteract and quench the inner fires that urged him to embrace the theatre wholly and exclusively. Instead, whether or no, that smoldering flame burst

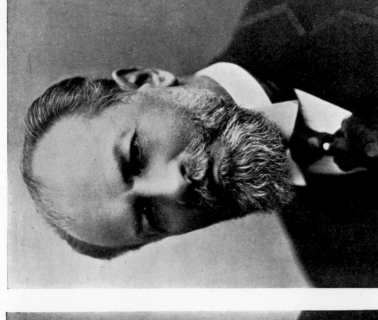

At the Opening of the Art Theatre, in 1908

On the Departure of the Musical Studio for America, 1925

VLADIMIR NEMIROVITCH-DANTCHENKO

Co-Founder, with Constantin Stanislavsky, of the Moscow Art Theatre and Sole Founder and Director of the Moscow Art Theatre Musical Studio

NEMIROVITCH-DANTCHENKO AT HIS DESK IN THE MOSCOW ART THEATRE

SUMMERING IN THE CRIMEA

(Left to right) Prince Alexander Sumbatoff, Director of the Moscow Small State Theatre; Nikolai Teleshyoff, Playwright and Head of the Art Theatre Museum; Yekaterina Nikolaievna, and Her Husband, Nemirovitch-Dantchenko.

NEMIROVITCH-DANTCHENKO AT WORK AND AT PLAY

through, directed the hand of the playwright unconsciously to use all the expedients and apparatus of the theatre, even prompted the saturation of the auditorium with the odor of pines for his early play, "The Dark Forest," a trick which had at least the virtue of novelty forty years ago.

His first play to achieve production was "The Wild Rose," begun on a wager at the age of twenty-three and disclosed in October, 1882, on the stage of the Small Imperial Theatre in Moscow with a cast that would have satisfied Ostrovsky at his peak—Fedotova, Akimova, Sadovsky, Muzil and a dozen others, names to conjure with in the annals of the Russian Theatre. Here, too, the regisseur in the playwright appeared, for, without waiting for O'Neill, Jones and "Desire Under the Elms" to show the way, Nemirovitch-Dantchenko struck at the heart of the conventional methods of the Government theatres. In the words of a contemporary critic: "During the overture, the curtain rose and the audience saw the façade of a two-story stone house, a part of the wall of which was raised at the conclusion of the music to disclose the interior of the lower floor of the home where all of the play's action takes place."

Another early play, "The Happy Man," was a failure, but in "The Last Will" the author carried his skill and his repute a generous step forward. What a cast was gathered to interpret it on the stage of the Small Imperial Theatre! Yermolova, Fedotova, Nikulina, Akimova, Lyensky, Ribakoff and Sumbatoff! The entire Russian theatre today could not muster such an ensemble. The play itself was the first of a long series in which the dramatist brought to a head through vivid human portraits and close-knit, logical

[189]

action a number of vital ethical, philosophical and social problems. At no time, though, did he seek to solve those problems, for that would debase art to propaganda. In this play, therefore, he simply held up to scrutiny the human consequences of Russia's testamentary laws. This method became still clearer in "A New Affair," which won the coveted Griboyedoff prize in 1890, another humanization of an economic issue, wholly lacking in romance but universally acclaimed by critics and public.

By 1894 Nemirovitch-Dantchenko held an enviable position in the intellectual and artistic spheres of Moscow. He was a critic whose word could make or break a play; two of his own plays steadily held the boards in the Small Imperial Theatre's repertory; he was a novelist whose next volume was eagerly awaited; his artistic judgment and discrimination had been recognized by his appointment to the theatrical literary committee of the Government theatres; he had been invited to take charge of the dramatic courses in the Philharmonic School. Under the impulses of this burgeoning life, he began his next play, "Gold." The most brilliant audience in Moscow's memory gathered at its premiere the following year, and the play was hailed as the fulfillment of Tchehoff's prophecy six years before in a letter to A. N. Pleshcheieff, "that in time Nemirovitch-Dantchenko would become a genuine dramatist." But in this triumph of realism, which anticipated Ibsen's later technique by some years, there was a flaw. In the author's original manuscript, Valentina, the heroine, pursues a brave and difficult course in her struggle to free herself from the tentacles of great wealth and sets her spirit free in aimless wandering.

The actors in fear demanded a compromise and the author, yielding to them, arranged a marriage. Only years later, when "Gold" was revived at Nezlobin's Theatre, was the honesty of the Russian stage, thanks largely to the pioneer integrity of the Moscow Art Theatre, sufficient to tolerate the original version.

From the intense sobriety of "A New Affair" and "Gold," Nemirovitch-Dantchenko turned next to a light-hearted and optimistic comedy, "The Value of Life." This play, which won for him once more the Griboyedoff prize, was written, as the author explains, at a time when he "was living intensely." To live intensely for a Russian means to have all the avenues of life open for creative effort, to feel within one's self an inexhaustible reserve power. That he was already preparing for his true life work in the Art Theatre he probably did not suspect. But the energy which found that outlet bubbled over in advance in this, the next to the last play he was to write. Six seasons passed before his valedictory as a dramatist was presented on the stage of the theatre he had helped in the meantime to found. "In Dreams," it was called, and while it did not repeat the success of his earlier plays, it is notable for the upcropping of that lyric spirit which he had theretofore suppressed in his writings and which was to burst forth in full flower almost a fifth of a century later in the foundation of his Musical Studio.

I have said that in the stories of Nemirovitch-Dantchenko, the novelist bows to the dramatist. Just as surely in his plays, the dramatist bows to the regisseur. Thanks not only to his early and intimate association with the stage and its people but also, of course, to his deep and hardly suppressed instincts for the theatre he crowded his plays with rôles that sprang to life at the actor's touch. Similarly, for all their literary style, his manuscripts spurred the producer to unwonted creative power, for they carried their own prompt books replete with stimulating hints for achieving the desired mood, atmosphere, interpretation and rhythm. And conversely, in the words of Yury Soboleff, "If that critic was right who said in praise of his dramas that their construction reveals a *regisseur* in the author, then we may conclude that the series of brilliant productions of the Moscow Art Theatre were the creation of a *literary* regisseur."

The first breach in the wall against active participation in the theatre which Nemirovitch-Dantchenko had erected within himself, was made when in 1891 he accepted an invitation to take charge of the dramatic courses in the Moscow Philharmonic School. Duplicating unwittingly the principles which Stanislavsky was trying to apply at the same time in the Society of Art and Literature, and anticipating the tenets which they were jointly to build into the Art Theatre, the young writer, now turned teacher at the age of thirty-three, announced his program at the school to be "a just interpretation of the plays and the discovery of the individual capacities of the players." Today in Russia that program sounds like an old saw; it has been a foregone conclusion for years. But in Moscow and Petersburg in the '80's and '90's, the Government theatres, most of the private theatres and the schools turned out rubber-stamp actors very much in the manner of our own lackadaisical theatre. Encouragement over the warm response to his program turned to despair when he saw how his pupils, barely grounded in a new conception of their art, trickled out on graduation into the sands of the provincial companies, became discouraged by the mediocrity around them and forgot all they had learned.

He must have a theatre, he came to realize, to hold these pupils and preserve their awakened spirit. The difficulties in the way of such a theatre were tremendous. Anton Rubinstein, the composer, had voiced the despair of achieving such a theatre in these words: "We will sooner attain a constitution than the freedom of the theatres in the capitals." Various conferences to achieve this end came to naught until that famous eighteen-hour session with Stanislavsky at the Slaviansky Bazar in June, 1897, when the Moscow Art Theatre was conceived. The story of that extraordinary interview, the plans it set in operation, the summer of active preparation for the first season and the realization of long-cherished hopes with the premiere of "Tsar Fyodor Ivanovitch" on October 14, 1898, have been recounted so frequently and have received such ample and final record in Stanislavsky's biography that I shall not dwell on them here.

Furthermore, to trace in detail the specific influence of Nemirovitch-Dantchenko on the career of the Moscow Art Theatre—the alert literary discrimination, bold and cautious at the same time, forward-looking and sure-footed as an antelope in his native Caucasus, one might say; the molding hand of the regisseur who had fought to avoid the rôle and, yielding, devoted himself ecstatically to the task; the administrative genius which devised an organization that is stronger and more influential today than when it was a

[193]

plunging young revolutionary—to chart explicitly these services and functions is not the forte of this chapter or of this book. Such a record would be, in effect, a running history, season by season, of the Moscow Art Theatre, a record that has already been generously provided by Constantin Stanislavsky in "My Life in Art," with characteristically gracious and invariably fair credit to his great collaborator for the rôles he played. If that record is ever to be repeated with Nemirovitch-Dantchenko as the vantage point for surveying the field once more, it should be done by his own hand alone. Enough has been said to prove him amply fitted by ambition, experience and achievement to serve as artistic peer of Stanislavsky in their joint project.

Nevertheless, we should pause long enough to note outstanding points in the Art Theatre's annals where the artist and the regisseur in Nemirovitch-Dantchenko most emphatically expressed themselves. As a matter of fact, there are very few of the three- or four-score productions in which he did not have a hand. Those in which that hand was uppermost and, indeed, the sole controlling artistic agent include: Ibsen's "The Pillars of Society," "When We Dead Awaken," "Brand," "Rosmersholm" and "Ghosts"; Tchehoff's "Ivanoff," Dostoievsky's "The Brothers Karamazoff" and "Nikolai Stavrogin" ("The Possessed"); Andreieff's "Anathema," "Yekaterina Ivanovna" and "Thought"; Shakespeare's "Julius Cæsar," Tolstoy's "The Living Corpse" ("Redemption"), Ostrovsky's "Enough Stupidity in Every Wise Man," Hamsun's "At the Gate of the Kingdom," Merezhkovsky's "There Will Be Joy," Surgutchoff's "Autumn Violins," Naidyonoff's "The Walls," Youshkye-

vitch's "Miserere," and Tchirikoff's "At the Monastery."
The large number of plays by hitherto unknown authors in
this list testifies to the open mind and constructive policy of
the regisseur's literary-dramatic taste.

In fact, it is this peculiar combination of literary and
dramatic judgment, which his early training had only
sharpened, that characterizes most signally Nemirovitch-
Dantchenko's influence on the Art Theatre's esthetic record.
It was he who insisted on Tchehoff long before Stanislavsky
awakened to the secret of Anton Pavlovitch's subtle and
simple truth, although when Stanislavsky finally grasped the
secret he was an eager rival in his enthusiasm. It was
Nemirovitch-Dantchenko who fought the battle of Ibsen on
the Russian stage, finally achieving popular as well as critical
triumph with "Brand," after impressing only the critics for
a long time. It was he who detected in Dostoievsky the mine
of psychological treasure for the actor. It was he who
hit upon the proper tone for the production of Gorky's
"The Lower Depths," a service which the author acknowledged by writing in the presentation copy, "I am indebted
for half the success of this play to your mind and heart."
It was his discerning eye that saw value in the neglected
dramatic works of Turgenieff. It was he with his amazing
embodiment of the author's conception in "Anathema" who
won Andreieff for the theatre. It was he who sensed the
means by which both the historic and the artistic truth of
"Julius Cæsar" could be reconciled so that not only Cæsar's
Rome but also Shakespeare's Titanic characters, sharply
individualized, could live once more before modern eyes. A
prompt book of five volumes in the Art Theatre's museum

bears witness to his consuming passion for eloquent and revealing detail in this monumental production.

The question will naturally arise, on realization of this broad rôle which Nemirovitch-Dantchenko played in the theatre's purely artistic record, as to just what were his relationships with Stanislavsky. In the beginning, Stanislavsky was to have the artistic veto; his collaborator, the literary veto. But the hair was hard to split, and the two made up their minds to be singly responsible for each production entrusted to his care. Many of the finest jewels in the Art Theatre's crown, however, were cut by their working side by side at the regisseurs' table. And in the long view of history, as Soboleff points out, the two will probably be merged into a single legendary character—Stanislavsky-Nemirovitch-Dantchenko. Through a quarter of a century of coöperative effort, despite temporary differences, each complemented the other: Stanislavsky provided the color, the fantasy, the warm human touch, the exaltation of the spirit; Nemirovitch-Dantchenko, the literary and psychological design, the realistic warp and woof.

The infallible taste and discrimination of Vladimir Ivanovitch are nowhere more evident than in his home. Probably my greatest surprise on returning to Moscow last winter was to find that he and his wife and son were living in identically the same apartment, with the same number of rooms, as before the Revolution. Neither Soviet nor hoodlum had dared cross the door. As I have said before, respect for the man had protected the theatre; respect for the theatre had protected the man and his possessions. I never felt farther from the seething world of Revolution's capital than when

RACHMANINOFF'S "ALEKO"
With Text by Vladimir Nemirovitch-Dantchenko, from Pushkin's Poem "The Gypsies"

A Costume Sketch by Ivan Gremislavsky and Nikolai Iznar

I stood in his library and chose from his shelves books from every literature in the world by sliding back a door with the author's portrait set behind its glass, or when I entered Yekaterina Nikolaievna's drawing room, repository for the treasures of a gentleman and a gentlewoman of the world who had picked wisely in their travels.

Vladimir Ivanovitch has known the good things of life, despite his ceaseless labors. His table bears witness to the same relish and the same exacting taste as his book shelves. Notwithstanding the heartiness of his enjoyment of life, he is a devotee of the axiom that everything has its place. Discipline with Stanislavsky is a matter of instinct, of second nature; with Nemirovitch-Dantchenko, a law imposed by a conscious and self-controlling will. In the theatre, for himself as well as for his company, he tolerates nothing but the most austere régime. I shall not soon forget the consuming fire that lit his face and set his voice a-tremble when he came into his lower office, adjoining his loge, after the performance of "Carmencita and the Soldier," and found Olga Baklanova, still in costume and make-up of the Spanish gypsy, eagerly asking my opinion of the performance.

"This is a theatre!" were his withering words, "not an opera house!"

CHAPTER XVI

THE PATRIARCH

INSIDE the Moscow Art Theatre—in the corridors, in the dressing rooms, in the offices, in the restaurant, wherever two or more of the theatre's six hundred and sixty souls are gathered together—Nemirovitch-Dantchenko is Vladimir Ivanitch, the shortened and intimate form of Vladimir Ivanovitch. On these same lips, however, Stanislavsky is neither Constantin Sergeievitch or Constantin Sergeitch; he is The Old Man. This term of informal respect coupled with deep affection aptly phrases the rôle he has played in the theatre's life, for he is in deed and in spirit as well as in appearance the Patriarch, although four years younger than the partner of his life-work.

Without the stalwart frame, the benign countenance, the naïve simplicity and the dominating presence of Stanislavsky, I am confident that the success of the Moscow Art Theatre in America would not have been of the same caliber, even if of the same proportions. Both physically and spiritually he personified the theatre to our public, placing its efforts on a plane of genial dignity that appealed to both heart and mind. No one who was present at the performance of Balieff's Chauve-Souris given in honor of the company of the Art Theatre four days before their own premiere, is likely to forget that procession down the aisles of very un-

[198]

actorlike and self-contained men and women, headed longitu-
dinally and altitudinally by their Patriarch. And whenever,
after their season was started, the audience at a premiere or
a farewell, in other cities as well as in New York, remained
to cheer, it was Stanislavsky they demanded. Even if he
had not been in the evening's cast, he had to be present at
the final curtain just the same.

My purpose here is not to recount the episodes in Stanislavsky's career, for he has done that himself with a disarming and heart-warming frankness in his autobiography, "My
Life in Art." Seldom has an artist laid bare his inmost soul,
confessed his mistakes and failures and given credit for his
successes where credit is due, so simply and so honestly as he
has done in this record. I prefer, rather, to sketch the man,
the artist and the teacher in his daily round since the dramatic
company's return home, with a belated word on his true and
unique function in the achievements of the Art Theatre.

It has become the custom among correspondents returning
from Moscow to extend condolences to the Patriarch for the
way he has been "sidetracked" in the dizzy whirl toward the
"left wing." In these reports, largely the work of misdirected and over-eager enthusiasts for Meyerhold, the
Kamerny Theatre and even the Art Theatre's Musical
Studio, Stanislavsky is depicted as having been stranded with
his beloved realism not only by the critics and the public but
also by his lifelong associates in the theatre. These rumors
and reports, one and all, I deny emphatically. In many
cases, the wish is probably father to the thought, but it will
take a great deal more than wishing to displace Stanislavsky
and his realism from the respect and the affections of vast

portions of the Moscow populace. The gods of the moment are the younger and more pugnacious "-ists" and "-isms," but most of them will be dead and forgotten long before the subtle and revealing technique, which yielded "The Lower Depths," "The Cherry Orchard" and "The Blue Bird," is laid away in history. If anyone doubts whether the Patriarch has a faithful following to tide his cherished ideals through stormy waters, let him try to buy a ticket to a play in the traditional repertory just before curtain time!

The rumor that Stanislavsky has been shelved by his associates sounds even more ominous, but it is equally without foundation. Having its genesis in the emergency reorganization of the theatre's administrative and executive affairs under Nemirovitch-Dantchenko as dictator, this rumor disregards the fact that for years Stanislavsky's consuming ambition has been to find time and opportunity for experimenting with his "system" so that he may leave it behind him completed as a legacy to future generations of actors. This time and opportunity he now possesses—to such an extent that, over and above his appearances as an actor in the current repertory and his duties as a collaborating regisseur with Nemirovitch-Dantchenko in the revival of such works as "The Sorrows of the Spirit" *("Gore ot Uma")*, he is able to apply himself not only to his rôle of adviser to the Dramatic Studio and School, but also to resuming the task of developing his own Operatic Studio, which had to be abandoned during his two years in America.

To visit the Patriarch at his home is to see him at work. His waking hours are so scheduled and crowded that his home has been fitted up to include a Studio and stage with its own dressing rooms and library. The building, which stands in the Leontievsky Pereulok across the street from the Kustarny or Peasants' Museum, is one of the few structures dating prior to the Napoleonic fire and it has an air all its own. While I was in Moscow last winter, the Government delivered to Constantin Sergeitch the papers making it over to him for life. His private quarters are furnished with those massive Russian pieces that comport so well with his own gigantic frame. And in them he lives the life of the patriarch no less surely and no less picturesquely than he does in the theatre, with his family down to the tiniest grandchild and his intimate friends gathered round a laden dinner table which effectually obliterates the memories of the famine years. Here, then, is a lingering island of the expansive and informal life of the cultured merchant families of Moscow, from which Stanislavsky sprang—a life that has all but disappeared in the Soviet capital and a life that contrasts strongly with the no less cordial and bountiful but rather more formal customs in vogue in the home of Vladimir Ivanitch, that suave *homme du monde*.

I purposely timed my visit to Leontievsky Pereulok to see a rehearsal of several acts of "Yevgeny Onyegin" by the pupils of Stanislavsky's Operatic Studio. The birth of that child of his riper years he has recounted in Chapter LX of his autobiography, so I shall not go into its details here. It is enough to note that the same crisis in the Great State Theatre which led to Nemirovitch-Dantchenko's effort to collaborate with the directors of the Opera in reviving the lyric stage through direct contact with its established exponents, also marks the genesis of Stanislavsky's own private

venture into the same field. But while Nemirovitch-Dantchenko gave up in despair and set to work to make his own
lyric theatre, which was to grow into the Musical Studio,
Stanislavsky with characteristic patience and persistence held
grimly to the few young singers from the State Opera who
could afford to take time from earning their bread in the
famine years. An experimental performance of this
Operatic Studio preceded the trip abroad. And now he is
hard at work again, with a waiting list of pupils from among
the younger members of the Opera, eager to learn from him
the secrets of his system to apply them to their lyric art.

As readers of "My Life in Art" already know, Stanislavsky is tolerant of innovators and innovations, but for
himself he prefers traditional paths. It is inevitable, therefore, that his Operatic Studio contrasts sharply with
Nemirovitch-Dantchenko's Musical Studio in aims, methods
and results. As nearly as I could surmise from the portions
of Tchaikovsky's masterpiece which Stanislavsky showed me
at the hands of an eager group of young people performing
without make-up or costume, his aim is realism in opera—
the same realism on which the Moscow Art Theatre was
founded, or rather, that realism shot through with fantasy
which reaches its peak in "The Blue Bird." His methods are
in keeping. It is too early to speak surely of his results.
All I know is that the illusion of life on that tiny stage,
heightened by Tchaikovsky's music, was thrilling to a degree
I have seldom experienced in the theatre. I am told that
under Stanislavsky's methods, as thus far developed, this
exciting illusion somehow vanishes when the production is
transferred to a large stage and auditorium. Both the aims

and the methods, too, would probably not be applicable to lyric dramas that demand stylized treatment, while "Yevgeny Onyegin" seems made expressly for such treatment and the Russian historical operas might become lyric "Tsar Fyodors." A happy choice for experiment with these aims and methods is Belasco's "The Girl of the Golden West," with the Puccini music, which Stanislavsky is preparing with his Operatic Studio for presentation on the stage of the Gabima Theatre during the absence of its company from Russia.

What I suspect is that Stanislavsky has unwittingly hit upon a program for the lyric stage that is as revolutionary in its way as the one which Nemirovitch-Dantchenko, by concentrated effort and under the spur of congenial atmosphere in Moscow today, has carried through to full achievement. I say unwittingly, for it seems to me that Stanislavsky cleaves to a false ambition in trying to put his methods into practice in a theatre of the size customarily used for opera. If he will deliberately direct his genius to the creation of what we might call *grand opéra intime,* he may be able to fill a small stage and a small theatre with an intensity of lyric feeling and an illusion of intensified life that will amount to a new artistic form.

No, the Patriarch is not shelved. Wholly apart from the possible fruits of his present experiments with his "system" in the Dramatic Studio and with realism as applied to the opera, his gracious but exacting spirit pervades these walls even more potently than before his journey to distant lands.

Furthermore, as an echo of that journey, he cherishes the possibility of realizing his dream of gathering under his wing in Moscow a score of young American actors whom he promises to train into a group with the same ideals and the same capacities as the Moscow Art Theatre itself—and all in the space of two or three years. That the impulse toward this dream does not exist solely in the vision of Stanislavsky is evident from these lines written by a young American producer while the Moscow Art Theatre was still in this country:

"More than anything else I should like to gather together a little group and start work with this great organization as our model; a group that had reverence and sincerity of purpose, that placed achievement above everything else, that was ready and able to sit at the feet of Stanislavsky and learn; a group that might, some day, mean to our theatre what the Moscow players have meant to the stage of Russia."

Stanislavsky feels that he owes a debt to America. He regretted deeply that he could not accept one of the several invitations to remain and work with us. He counters, therefore, with an invitation for us to come and work with him. For he is just as convinced, as was Nemirovitch-Dantchenko with the Musical Studio, that only inside the walls of the Art Theatre under the sway of its standards and its traditions, can he train a company of American players to the point where they will do honor to their instruction.

CHAPTER XVII

The Family of the Art Theatre

The Moscow Art Theatre, with all its divisions and sub-divisions, its reorganizations and its growing taste for world-wandering, is, after all, one great family. I doubt whether the history of the world's theatres can show another instance where so large a group of actors and stage craftsmen have lived and labored together so intimately for so long a time. As I write these lines, the twenty-seventh anniversary of the theatre's birth is being celebrated in the Russian capital. The same two artists who founded it are still in control of its destinies. Still associated with them are upwards of a dozen of its charter members. The personnel has grown from a single company and a handful of young novices in the art of the theatre to a comity of four companies and over 600 workers trained in their profession as few groups have ever been trained in the annals of the stage. In the course of the Art Theatre's career, there have been losses by secession and death. But the nucleus has remained and expanded. Of the six hundred and more participants today, the vast majority have been working side by side for from five to thirty-five years, for it must be remembered that the Art Theatre was created by the merging of two amateur groups who already had to their credit years of coöperative effort together. And

[205]

yet, despite this expansion to the proportions of an entire village, the spirit and atmosphere of intimate fellowship have been preserved.

The great secret of the strength of these family ties is the same secret that explains the enigma of how these Russians learned to act. "The answer," wrote George Jean Nathan in reference to this latter question, "is peculiarly simple, and consists of one word. That word is 'work.' The Russians look on acting as a job, like plumbing, masonry or bridge building, and devote their mornings, noons, nights and years to doing that job as perfectly as it is in their power to do it." And there is nothing that binds men and women together, nothing that gives them clearer understanding and deeper sympathy with each other, than mutual labor on a given task—not even playing together or living with one another. Then, second only to the consuming intensity of their joint labors, is the humanization of those labors : dressing rooms, as I explained in Chapter I, that are all but home; ample recreation parlors; rehearsals held in congenial surroundings, not on a strange stage cluttered with someone else's scenery; simple, wholesome food always ready in the theatre's own restaurant; a repertory system whereby, in the first place, the monotony of playing the same rôle night after night is avoided and, in the second, the actor is free from any public duty from one to three evenings a week. Furthermore, the various branches of the family are kept on intimate and cordial terms by the practice of visiting performances on each others' stages.

In view of these facts, the choice of the players who visited us is at least intelligible. Nothing but nostalgia could have persuaded many of them to reject handsome offers from the motion pictures and the speaking stage and return to Moscow to receive as many rubles a month as they had drawn in dollars a week in this country, meager as this latter sum was. Some moved back into the homes they had occupied for years. Others found their old quarters preëmpted or curtailed through Moscow's desperate housing shortage. Olga Knipper-Tchehova, for instance, returned to her modest rooms overlooking the wooded expanse of the Pretchistensky Boulevard. Here she had resumed life amid the treasured mementoes of the author of "The Cherry Orchard"—photographs on the walls and editions of his works in a half dozen different languages on the shelves. A nephew, one or two other relatives and a friend or two from the company share the tiny apartment with her to prevent total strangers being assigned to the extra rooms.

Katchaloff and his wife, Litovtseva, on the other hand, had to be content with a quaint bandbox in a building owned by the theatre, occupied by the carpenter shop on the ground floor and set back in the courtyard behind the main structure. Crowded as he is, the Baron of "The Lower Depths" lives in the picturesque atmosphere of other days, for these walls must have seen a century; and besides he is only a hundred paces from his work. Here, after the evening of Tchehoff's "Hamlet," we had an "American" reunion—Ambassador cigarettes with the American flag on the box, a favorite brand in the Russian capital today; very un-American vodka and Russian champagne; and fond reminiscences of the distant land of yesterday and overseas. And it was here that Olga Knipper-Tchehova humbled her dignified host by telling how he had run aground on the American language one night in Boston. Katchaloff, it seems, was accustomed to beguiling many an idle hour and improving his knowledge of American city planning at the modest cost of five, six, seven or ten cents for a round trip ride on a street car. Late one evening in Boston the car didn't make the round trip, and the conductor's "All out!" left the exploring actor stranded in a distant suburb. A drug store light beckoned, and Katchaloff entered, summoning from his vocabulary of a dozen English phrases the word "Taxi!"

The apothecary, eager to serve, was equally laconic with the word "Five!"

With visions of a crisp bank note as the price of his excursion, but game withal, he agreed, "All right."

Something was wrong, however, for the druggist kept repeating "Five!" and held up his hand to prove it, while the taxi seemed to be as remote as ever. Finally the man behind the counter had a bright idea. He went to his cash register, rang up "no sale," extracted a nickel and pointed to the telephone booth. Relieved to find the process so simple, Katchaloff tapped his own cash register, waited while his rescuer hailed a nearby garage and ultimately reached his hotel.

It is not in the intimate foregatherings around a groaning dinner table, however, or over a midnight repast of caviar, cold fish and vodka, that the family aspects of the Art Theatre emerge most clearly. The imposing proportions and the strong bonds of this brotherhood of over six hundred become evident, rather, on occasions when they function as a single body. Such an occasion was the celebration, shortly before my arrival last winter, of the centenary of the Small State Theatre, in which the Moscow Art Theatre participated in full force, marching through the streets of the capital and very nearly equaling the representatives of all the other theatres combined.

The close-knit skeins of this great fraternity were even more vividly and poignantly attested in the sad but beautiful and picturesque Russian ceremonies attendant upon the sudden and untimely death of Giorgi Burdzhaloff during my stay in Moscow. Burdzhaloff is cherished by countless Americans as Kostilyoff, the wizened and sinister old keeper of the Night Lodging in "The Lower Depths," a rôle which he had played 475 times and which no one else but he had played since the premiere in December, 1902. During my first week in Moscow, I had returned to the Art Theatre for the latter half of "Tsar Fyodor." Burdzhaloff lavished his ripe talents on the minor rôle of Prince Vassily Shouisky, the same rôle in which he had helped the theatre make its bow to the Moscow public away back in 1898. After the final curtain, as I was trying to talk in four languages to Katchaloff in his dressing room, Giorgi Sergeievitch, with half his make-up still on, came to the door, helped us out and plied me with questions regarding America, Morris Gest, and his old comrade, Nikita Balieff, whose London premiere I had just seen. Excusing himself shyly, he went home, never to reënter those beloved walls again, for that night he was seized with a heart attack and less than a week later he was cold in death.

The shock that ran through the entire theatre next morning is indescribable. So is the ominous foreboding of the week of waiting. Men and women talked in the corridors in whispers, although the wheels of the institution moved round relentlessly. The Art Theatre's prime responsibility was to its public; its anxiety and its grief were private, a secret of the hearthstone. Probably no one in the family, save Stanislavsky and Nemirovitch-Dantchenko, had been so near and dear to that hearthstone as Burdzhaloff. Born in 1869 in Astrahan of Armenian parentage, he spent five years with Stanislavsky's Society of Art and Literature before the founding of the Art Theatre and was chosen housekeeper during that far-away but never-forgotten summer of preparation for the new venture in Pushkino. His acting rôles were seldom outstanding—the Marquis in "The Mistress of the Inn," the Pole Musyalovitch in "The Brothers Karamazoff," the First Guest in "Ivanoff," and Gislesen in Hamsun's "In the Claws of Life," in the American repertory, besides the two I have already mentioned; Fire in "The Blue Bird," the Green Grandfather in "Peer Gynt," Mr. N. in "The Sorrows of the Spirit," Rostakovsky in "The Inspector General," the Clergyman in "Lonely Lives," and Karela in "Boris Godunoff." But his rôle in the life of the theatre was dominant. Tremendous faith was reposed in his integrity and he was the perennial president of the board of auditors. In lighter vein, he helped manage the "cabbage nights" when everyone, including Stanislavsky, buried his dignity and donned cap and bells. Moreover, his first wife was the theatre's flaming talent, the mourned Savitskaya.

On the day before the funeral private grief became public. While the closest friends' crowded the little apartment a block and a half from the theatre, the bowed ranks of the whole

THE LATE GIORGI BURDZHALOFF

In the Rôle of Prince Vassily Shouisky in "Tsar Fyodor Ivanovitch," in Which He Opened and Closed His Career with the Moscow Art Theatre

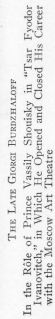

VLADIMIR YERSHOFF

As Prince Shakhovskoy in "Tsar Fyodor," Now Playing the Commanding Rôle of Boris Bodunoff as Reward for Fidelity in Refusing Tempting Offers to Remain in America

In the Title Rôle
Of Tchehoff's "Ivanoff"

In Life

VASSILY KATCHALOFF—MASK AND MAN

As the Baron
In Gorky's "The Lower Depths"

600 gathered in the street below and under lowering December skies trudged off across the city behind the coffin to the little Armenian church. Only the solicitations of Yekaterina Nikolaievna were effective in persuading Nemirovitch-Dantchenko to drop out of line, while Stanislavsky with bared white head trudged the clammy cobblestones to the end of the route. Next morning, under a cold and reluctant sun, the cortège retraced its steps to the burial ground on the opposite confines of Moscow. A line of march leading through the Street of the Moscow Art Theatre was chosen, while under the Sea-Gull portal the orchestra of the Musical Studio huddled in wait for the signal that the procession approached. Then, as the priests came in sight, in defiance of the Soviet ban on public religious display and in costumes that might have been taken from the wardrobe of "Tsar Fyodor," the band wailed the wild and bitter funeral march from "Hamlet" which Ilya Sats had composed for the Gordon Craig production. And as the dear comrade passed forever out of sight of the theatre that had been his home, all of Russia's greatest actors and artists joined the cavalcade as members of the Art Theatre's sorrowing family. For quaint and traditional postlude, the marchers, chilled to the marrow, found awaiting them, in the theatre's restaurant on their return, huge heaps of Russian pancakes, served with sour cream, the age-old symbol of the end of the wake.

The forethought which remembered that ceremony of the cakes, the hand which turned them, were those of Prokofieff, the modest, silent, chunky little monarch whose kingdom is the Art Theatre's restaurant. Through this restaurant, a public rendezvous between the acts of an evening, the retreat of the parents, uncles, aunts, children and grandchildren of the multitudinous family by day, flows the life-blood of the Art Theatre. Established originally for the convenience of the theatre's patrons, it was expanded to serve the theatre's workers as well during the early days of the Revolution when Prokofieff's skill in buying kept scores from starvation. Ever since then, the restaurant has been the theatre's club-house, its play-room, its newspaper. Luncheon—or break-fast, if you like to call it that, Russian fashion—at noon. Dinner from late afternoon until six. And tea from a samovar as big as a sugar barrel, time and quantity without end. Seated on his stool-throne behind the counter, with a nod of welcome or a "Health to you!" the little round man superintends the dispensation of these bounties more like a godfather than a tsar or a restaurateur.

For Prokofieff too, you see, has been a member of the family of the Art Theatre since its foundation. Back in those summer days of 1898 at Pushkino, he was the young man who brought the fruits and vegetables and meats and great Russian loaves and served as caterer to the youthful Argonaut-actors. Thereafter his fortunes fluctuated. At one time he was the concessionaire in a dozen Moscow theatres. Then misfortune left him penniless, a state from which the Art Theatre rescued him by a benefit performance. Latterly, his star has risen again, for today he has buffets in the foyers of all three buildings operated by the Art Theatre and in a number of other theatres, besides catering for the sumptuous restaurant cars on the Russian railroads left behind by the *Compagnie Internationale des Wagon-Lits et des Grands Express Européens* and recently restored to service by the Soviet.

Still, despite his manifold interests, Prokofieff's persistent haunt is the Art Theatre, his unofficial office the little stool behind the counter in the restaurant of his favorite godchild. There he sits, day after day, helping his protégés, young and old, to choose the tastiest and most wholesome food that his ingenuity and skill have been able to devise—and all of it charged up on the books at cost or less than cost. When trade slackens and the hum of busy voices floats through the restaurant doors from the corridors and lobbies beyond, Prokofieff slips silently from his stool, tiptoes carefully along the carpeted passageways and peers cautiously behind first one screen and then another, erected to protect player groups absorbed simultaneously in different rehearsals. Then, the rounds made, Prokofieff returns to his stool. The godfather of the family of the Art Theatre is satisfied that all is well!

CHAPTER XVIII

ART THEATRE, SOVIET AND PUBLIC

LIKE all families in a civilized state, the family of the Moscow Art Theatre is constrained to fulfill certain public relations. No matter how much it may wish, as a fraternity of artists, to live to itself, to ignore all factors in life save the esthetic, it can not escape the fundamental responsibilities, privileges and contacts with Government and with populace. In conclusion, therefore, it seems fitting to survey these public relations calmly and dispassionately, in order to counteract, if possible, the hysteria, both for and against, with which Americans greet every arrival from Russia.

An atmosphere of anxiety, a sense of suspicion, have always hovered over the Russian theatre. The mystery of apprehension and foreboding is just as distinctively characteristic of Russian life as the white nights of summer, the bitter pall of winter, the expanse of the steppes. Relieve a Russian of these premonitions, and he conjures up new ones. For this reason, a great deal of sympathy has been wasted on the victims of Soviet surveillance by a world unaccustomed to the psychology of the Russian mind and suddenly confronted with its vagaries.

From its earliest days, the censor has stood strict guard over the Russian stage. Griboyedoff never saw a performance of his masterpiece, *"Gore ot Uma"* or "The Sorrows of

the Spirit," whose centenary was celebrated by its revival
at the Art Theatre last season. He never saw it printed in
full, and thirty-six years elapsed before the liberal Tsar
Alexander II permitted complete publication and production. After him, hardly a playwright missed falling foul of
the Government's intolerance. Entire manuscripts by
Andreieff were suppressed. Even so harmless a satire as
Saltuikoff's "The Death of Pazuhin" was known only in
garbled form for years. And yet the drama and the theatre
flourished, partly because of the challenge of repression and
partly because the subtlety and flexibility of the art of the
theatre gave it more freedom, after all, than literature.

As a result, Stanislavsky's description of a performance
of "An Enemy of the People," the night after the massacre
in Kazanskaya Square during the Art Theatre's first season
in Petersburg, is not unique but typical of a century's annals
on the Russian stage.

"The performance," he writes, "was more political than
artistic. The atmosphere in the theatre was such that we
expected arrests at any minute and a stop to the performance.
Censors, who sat at all the performances of 'An Enemy of
the People' and saw to it that I, who played Doctor Stockmann, should use only the censored text, and raised trouble
over every syllable that was not admitted by the censorship,
were on this evening even more watchful than on other occasions. I had to be doubly careful. When the text of a rôle
is cut and recut many times, it is not hard to make a mistake
and say too much or too little."

But the sky only rumbled until Stockmann's line in the last
act: "A man should never put on his best trousers when he

[215]

goes out to battle for freedom and truth." Then the storm broke. The art of the theatre fled through the stage door, while both auditorium and stage became a street-corner mob. "From that evening on," writes Stanislavsky, "many attempts were made to drag our Theatre into politics, but we, who knew the true nature of the Theatre, understood that the boards of our stage could never become a platform for the spread of propaganda, for the simple reason that the very least utilitarian purpose or tendency, brought into the realm of pure art, kills art instantly."

Today there is still the censorship, apparently with diametrically opposite aims—for the plays that used to be banned are now subsidized, and vice versa—but in reality with identically the same goal. (Censorship in Russia, we must remember, has never been a matter of public morals. It has nothing to do with Mrs. Grundy, profanity, religious prejudice or visibility of the human form. It was—and is— primarily concerned by the process of veto with the preservation and safety of the existing Government, and secondarily by the process of propaganda with the cultivation of a social, political and esthetic ideology conducive to that safety. The chief difference between the old censorship and the new is that the Tsarist watchdogs were content with exercising the direct or veto function upon intransigence, while the Soviet devotes at least as much if not more attention to fostering proletarian propaganda as it does to smothering everything hostile to the proletarian state.)

Under both the old censorship and the new, the Moscow Art Theatre has clung doggedly to its artistic independence by strict observation of the axiom Stanislavsky enunciated in the last paragraph but one. Artists less earnest, less sure of their footing, might have resented deeply the fact that they could not produce such a play as Andreieff's "Savva" under the Tsar. But with the same profound understanding of the true nature of art which formulated this axiom, they undoubtedly saw that the very factors which rendered a play suspicious in the eyes of Government—"propaganda," "utilitarian purpose or tendency"—made it dubious from the angle of esthetics. If they were resentful, their irritation was not directed against the Government as such but against a general state of mind under which a work of art assumed "utilitarian" implications and thus, as it were, suffered artistic murder.

Likewise, if one can accept the Soviet contention that Tchehoff today is bourgeois and anti-Government propaganda, "The Cherry Orchard" and "The Three Sisters" would drop outside an art theatre's repertory automatically and without argument. It is not easy to accept this contention, nor, for that matter, is it easy to specify just what bourgeois propaganda is. Revolutionary propaganda is unmistakable; counter-revolutionary, elusive. Still, even if this contention seems absurd and groundless—as it does to everyone who understands and loves Tchehoff's serene spirit—the mere fact that the Soviet deems it true, no matter how mistakenly, indicates a state of mind in which Tchehoff becomes tantamount to propaganda. His subtle and fragile beauties have been dragged into the public forum and tagged as symbols of a bourgeois idealism. And rather than submit its patron saint to the indignities of a raucous argument, the Art Theatre has quietly laid him on the shelf.

Not only has Stanislavsky's axiom helped to reconcile the Art Theatre to the overt vetoes of both Tsar and Soviet, but it has protected the theatre to a large extent from petty interference. Neither Nikolai Romanoff nor Nikolai Lenin nor any of their ministers ever tried to tell the Art Theatre *what* to produce or *how* to produce it. Private busybodies have tried, but the reading of the axiom put them to rout. Informers have probably sat in the theatre's most secret councils; the man who helps you with your coat may be listening with both ears and eyes. It wouldn't be Russia without informers or without the mystery and dread of wondering which of your associates is cast for that rôle. But there is nothing untoward to hear or to see. Living its axiom as well as professing it and asking no favors or dispensations, the Moscow Art Theatre has enjoyed immunity from intrusion and has won and held the respect that makes for independence, through the old years of financial autonomy, through the months of economic expropriation by the Soviet in the early stages of the Revolution, and during the ensuing return to private management.

That jealously guarded independence, however, counted for naught in the eyes of the American Defense Society. With all the terror of a war-time spy-hunt, this organization sought to forestall the Art Theatre's sailing by imputing to it malign subservience to the Soviet Government. American intelligence rushed to the defense not only of the awaited visitors but of our reputation for national sanity. Augustus Thomas, for the Producing Managers' Association, and Frank Gillmore, for the Actors' Equity Association, deplored the attack on Stanislavsky and his players, the latter writing:

"Our sentiment can be best understood from our action in making them all honorary members of our association during their visit to America."

Speaking as Honorary Chairman in behalf of the Committee of Patrons for the American season of the Moscow Art Theatre, Otto H. Kahn issued the following statement:

"I sympathize with the motives and the aim of the American Defense Society, but Americanism is not so frail a growth that it needs to be protected from contact with the Moscow Art Theatre.

"The visit of that organization can not, by any remote stretch of the imagination, be connected with Soviet propaganda. It is an event of distinct significance, but that significance is solely and wholly of an artistic character.

"By common consent, the Moscow Art Theatre stands supreme among organizations devoted to dramatic art. It is looked upon with something resembling reverence by leaders of the dramatic profession in all countries. Its repertory here will consist entirely of plays of the Russian classical repertory.

"The Moscow Art Theatre has just completed a two weeks' season in Paris. Among all the world's Governments, none has been more determined in discountenancing the Soviet Government than that of France. No people has been, and is, more opposed to Bolshevism than the French people. No authorities are more strict in controlling the admission of Russians, than those in charge of the issuance of passports to France.

"Yet, the French Government not only permitted the visit of the Moscow Art Theatre to Paris, but the artists composing that troupe were treated with distinguished consideration in official quarters. The people and the press of Paris were unanimous in the manifestation of their enthusiasm anent the performances of these artists.

"Our own Government, which has permitted the viséing of the passports of the Moscow Art Theatre artists to this country, would certainly have refused to do so if its own investigation had not fully convinced it that there is no relationship whatsoever, open or hidden, direct or indirect, between the aims and activities of these visitors and the aims and activities of Bolshevist propaganda.

"Whether a certain proportion of the earnings of the artists of the Moscow Art Theatre is payable to the Soviet Government, as stated by the American Defense Society, I do not know. If it is so, that is no different from the practice prevailing here, under which the earnings of artists, both American and foreign, in this country, are liable to income taxation. Should we cease to eat Russian caviar because the Soviet Government derives a revenue from its production?"

Next day, the New York *World* commented editorially, just as emphatically but far more ironically, under the heading "Great Plot Discovered":

"The ever-vigilant American Defense Society has discovered another plot to overthrow the American Government. The plot is to be perpetrated by the Moscow Art Theatre, which sails today for New York. The plot is sponsored by such eminent Bolshevists as Mr. Otto H. Kahn, Chairman; Dr. Nicholas Murray Butler, Mr. Paul Cravath, Dr. John Grier Hibben, Mr. Thomas W. Lamont and Mr. Clarence Mackay.

"These tools of Lenin had not read the contract signed by the Art Theatre. But now it is exposed by the American Defense Society.

"According to that contract, these dangerous artists have agreed not to conduct propaganda against the Soviets. But 'special preference is shown those who agree to conduct propaganda for the Soviets.' The special preference seems to lie in the chance to be fired by Morris Gest for breach of contract if they do any such thing.

"They agree to pay 33 per cent. of their earnings to the Russian Government. This is a fairly high income tax, and the American Defense Society's heart bleeds for these poor Russians.

"Finally, they agree to return to Russia. This is the plot of plots and will stamp the Moscow Art Theatre for all time as one of the most sinister bodies that ever attacked this Republic.

"Having exposed the plot, the American Defense Society, true to its heroic traditions, invites the American Legion to rise to the defense of America. Just what it would like the Legion to do is not clear, but the general impression made by the Society's pronouncement is that a little lawlessness would not seem to it undesirable.

"It is an idiotic performance. A society organized to make propaganda for preparedness in the midst of a great war finds itself fighting an art theatre. . ."

Not satisfied with being laughed out of court in the nation's metropolis, the American Defense Society broadcast malicious insinuations behind the Art Theatre's back on tour. R. M. Whitney, its Director, repeated the charges in the

[221]

Boston Evening Transcript of May 24, 1923, finally stirring the modest and taciturn but incorruptible Stanislavsky to this naïve but ringing denial:

"The only propaganda we are engaged in in this country is art-propaganda; we are under no financial obligation whatsoever to the Soviet Government; the only 'tax' we are to undergo is a certain sum which we will give to the Committee of Relief for the hunger-stricken departments of Russia—that sum being much smaller than the large amount due to the generosity of the American people. We infinitely regret that we are not even in the position to give as much as was raised for the same aim on the single event of a dinner given in Chicago in my presence by the representatives of the American Relief Administration. . . .

"I take this opportunity to express once more my deepest sentiment of gratitude to the American public and press, who did not mistake us for what we are not, but paid us a never-to-be-forgotten tribute for that which we are."

Why do I go into this past history at such length? Partly for the sake of the record, but far more because the same bogey is likely to arise in connection with the visit of the Art Theatre's Musical Studio. The members of this company are young; they have grown to manhood and to womanhood under the régime of Lenin and his heirs. The American Defense Society, heartened by the example of American intolerance in the cases of Karolyi and Saklatvala, is likely to "discover" that the Soviet now subsidizes the Moscow Art Theatre. And is not that more heinous than taking the toll of taxes? And finally there is the matter of a vast petition signed by thousands of innocent Americans and

addressed to Anatoly V. Lunatcharsky, Minister of Education (and incidentally of Fine Arts and the Theatre), re-
questing leave of absence from Russia for the Musical Studio
and permission for it to come to America.

To all this, there is but one answer: The Moscow Art
Theatre in all its branches abides rigidly and doggedly by the
axiom outlawing all propaganda, which Stanislavsky formulated over twenty-five years ago.

Two factors have operated to fortify this obstinate stand
for artistic independence during the trying years since 1917.
One of them is the respect, not to say reverence, in which
the Moscow public holds the Art Theatre; the other is the
high regard for its achievements on the part of Lunatcharsky. In spite of all the efforts of the apologists of the "new
school" to discredit the fountain head of the modern Russian
stage abroad and at home, to dub it "passé" and "antiquated,"
and to read a patronizing funeral oration over its remains,
the Moscow Art Theatre today is busier, more significant,
more influential, more deeply and widely cherished than it
has ever been in its long career. I have already recounted in
Chapter I how the enormous demand for seats at the height
of the season has revived the old lottery scheme of distribu-
tion. Furthermore, the Art Theatre is the only one in all
Russia where the demand justifies the ticket speculator to
operate on the sidewalk. (And, by the way, the Soviet has
been no more successful than our American police in discouraging the practice!) All this, it must be remembered, in
the face of a box office scale that would frighten the most
careless Broadway "spender." I give here, for the sake of
interesting comparisons, the scale of prices on the theatre's

[223]

opening night, on its twenty-fifth anniversary in the mael-
strom of the currency inflation, and today. Keep in mind,
if you will, that to the Russian the pre-war ruble and the
ruble of 1925 is, for all practical purposes save international
exchange, the equivalent of a dollar.

October 14/27, 1898
Parterre—5 rubles 50 kopecks to 90 kopecks
Balcony—1 ruble 30 kopecks to 65 kopecks
Gallery—70 kopecks to 25 kopecks

October 14/27, 1923
Parterre—3 billion to 500 million rubles
Balcony—2 billion to 300 million rubles
Gallery—1 billion to 100 million rubles

Today
Parterre—7 to 3 rubles
Balcony—6 rubles to 1 ruble 50 kopecks
Gallery—4 rubles to 50 kopecks

Willingness to pay these prices, however, is only one form
of the esteem of the Moscow populace for the Art Theatre.
A more potent, if less tangible, manifestation of this attitude
is the protecting circle which public veneration has drawn
round the theatre and its presiding geniuses. That circle has
functioned in two ways: Respect for the Art Theatre has
safeguarded the person and the property of both Stanislavsky
and Nemirovitch-Dantchenko. Love and respect for its
founders have sheltered the theatre. As Morris Gest put it
in answering the charges of the American Defense Society:
"For their art they defied the Soviet Government, even
through the years between 1919 and 1921, when the Govern-

ment took over and ran all the theatres. At the risk of prison, they persisted in playing their old established repertory and out of fear of the theatre's clientele in Moscow, the Government dared not raise a hand against them."

All of these years, however, there has been a friend at court, a quiet, scholarly apologist. Some might even call him a pedant, if they merely observed the careful way in which he documents all his arguments. His name is Anatoly Vassilievitch Lunatcharsky, whose restraining hand has saved even the Kremlin's double eagles, wrought of gold by Ivan the Terrible, as I have told in Chapter IV. As an instance of Lunatcharsky's regard for the Moscow Art Theatre and of his deep interest in the philosophical problems propounded by its productions, I have saved to spread on record here, rather than in the chapter on "Carmencita and the Soldier," the correspondence between him and Nemirovitch-Dantchenko relative to the esthetic issues raised by the regisseur's innovations.

Moscow, U. S. S. R.,
May 16, 1925.

To the National Artist of the Republic,
Vladimir Ivanovitch Nemirovitch-Dantchenko.
Dear Vladimir Ivanovitch :

I know that today marks the fifth anniversary of your work in the field of the musical theatre. I wish you to receive tonight the expression of my opinion of your merits and those of your collaborators in your versatile activities in the realm of the theatre.

I know your real purposes, I know the full reach of your ideas and plans, and I know that you have thus far materialized only a small part of them. Long ago I expressed one of my most cherished dreams when I said that the noblest form of the theatre comprises a living amalgamation of the spoken word and music, that the true atmosphere of dramatic action presupposes such an amalgamation. Of course, in saying this, I do not reject the possibilities of opera in one form or another. But not one of the older forms of opera, not excluding Wagnerian mysteries or the efforts of the realists to create music drama, has ever satisfied me. It is understood that this musical-dramatic theatre will be versatile and many-sided, will possess something fundamental, an exaltation of life on the wings of music to a sublime and boundless plane, which subordinates the dissonances of the spoken word and the discords of the human rhythm to one inclusive, immanent, measured rhythm—the rhythm which is possible only in the sphere of music.

In your first operettas you created a gorgeous magnetic spectacle, which uplifted the comic opera, in the sense of artistic accomplishment, to heights never before attained. Vast horizons have unfolded before you on the peaks which you have scaled. I remember well when you said that the work of a stage director of productions without music seemed to you dull and lacking in any cohesive spirit.

"Lysistrata" was an achievement of very great importance. The reviewers on our daily newspapers did not fully comprehend its importance, but of course it will be understood by the historians of our contemporary theatre. The external shaping and staging of the libretto, in which you managed to surpass the most daring accomplishments of the "left wing" theatre and in which you passed the play through

"CARMENCITA AND THE SOLDIER"
Sketch of a Chorus Group by Isaac Rabinovitch

the prism of refined taste and academic learning in the best sense of the word, is absolutely amazing. Also as a step toward the desired theatre of the musical drama—in this case, in the cross-section of high comedy—the performance won deserved attention.

To many, "Carmencita and the Soldier" seemed doubtful. I, too, have not yet fully accepted it. I understand which aspect of the drama of Mérimée-Bizet attracted most of your attention and compelled you to make a profound experiment in the creation of a sort of philosophical musical tragedy. The mordant realism of this story, which discloses the deep and throbbing secret heart of human nature, naturally commanded your consideration. But the music of Bizet, written, to my mind, with the purpose of elevating the libretto to a larger external festival brilliancy, may be a mistake of Bizet; but I have no doubt that he wrote his score on the plot of the love between Carmen and José, and that he wrote it as a grand opera—a masterly, unusual grand opera, but after all a grand opera. And that is why it is difficult to accept without reservation your exaltation of this production to a higher level, your adaptation of a brilliant musical festival, wherein at the grand opera houses we are invariably conquered by a dainty Carmen, into a profound musical tragedy intensified to the last degree.

Despite this, I consider your adaptation of "Carmen" of great significance. No doubt, it is possible to discern in this production the interesting forerunner of the future theatre. No doubt, here is a real tragedy as a starting point on the road to that theatre of the future, a tragedy which is an example of refined taste and a search for new theatrical forms. "Carmencita and the Soldier" must be acknowledged as an event of the highest importance.

I congratulate you for having added this beautiful flower in your work in the field of the musical theatre to your fertile achievement in the dramatic theatre. People may think that this is simply a rose in the lapel of your conservative *habit noir,* but in reality it is a new flight of your searching talent for the theatre toward the heights of your ideal theatre.

Kindly deliver my congratulations also to all your collaborators who walk with you hand in hand on this new and difficult path.

In view of the necessity of economizing its forces in order to assist the most essential group of theatres on a larger scale than in the past, the Government has recently raised a question regarding the vitality of the Moscow Art Theatre Musical Studio. In reply to that question, I assured them most emphatically that in the constricted family of the academic theatres of our Republic, you have won a secure place.

I shake your hand cordially.

> (Signed) A. LUNATCHARSKY,
> Minister of Education.

> May 27, 1925,
> Moscow.

Dear Anatoly Vassilievitch:

Once more I am writing to you about my "Carmencita and the Soldier"—a little argument in reference to your wonderful letter to me of May 16th.

You stress the point that Bizet's "Carmen" is a true grand opera.

On this very point I detect a widespread error which

emanated from the Great State (Bolshoy) Theatre and other homes of grand opera.

In "Carmen," Bizet wrote an intimate little opera in keeping with the intimacy of Mérimée's novel. He wrote it for the Opéra-Comique in Paris, where it was first produced. He wrote it for a small orchestra, a small chorus. I would recommend to you that you give your attention some time to the intervals of the third act where, for instance, only a single flute plays, and if you listen to the orchestra of the Great State Theatre playing "Carmen," you'll feel the superfluous force in some of these same instruments. Perhaps that is necessary in view of the size of the auditorium, but it is prejudicial to the musical essence of these individual intervals. As for the chorus, there is nothing to say. What can you imagine more absurd than a hundred smugglers in the mountains! There remains only the circus parade. This episode occurs at the beginning of the last act—the only shadow of an excuse for us to consider this a grand opera.

Moreover, the most valuable element in Bizet is the close intimacy and intensity of personal feelings, not of the mob, not of the ensemble, but of Carmencita and especially of José.

In some workmen's theatrical paper, I have read several times that in "Carmen" the theatre should depict the life of the factory working-women. That is ridiculous! Whence does that impression arise? Simply because the first act (as in the beginning of Mérimée's novel) brings in groups of cigarette makers—only two choruses!

Have you happened to run across the letters of Nietzsche on "Carmen"?

[229]

I take the liberty of enclosing a quotation which I print in the programs.

Devotedly yours,

(Signed) VL. NEMIROVITCH-DANTCHENKO.

With this glimpse into the mental processes of the Minister of Education—leaves out of an intimate and continuing correspondence, not a solitary salutation saved for celebrations of fifth anniversaries and the like—it becomes clearer not only why he is a confirmed believer in the worth of the Moscow Art Theatre's contribution to the annals of Russian art and culture but also why he has been able by dialectic and persuasion to impress the hard-headed doctrinaires of the Soviet's Central Executive Committee with the necessity of non-interference in its affairs and support of its endeavors.

If Lunatcharsky, on his part, is frankly outspoken in his regard for the Moscow Art Theatre, Nemirovitch-Dantchenko is no less frank in admitting that only under the restless experimental atmosphere and the breathless pace of revolution could he have crystallized so speedily his long-cherished dream of renovating the lyric stage. Prejudices, preconceptions, the shackles of tradition, no longer existed. Neither did standards. But Nemirovitch-Dantchenko was ready to erect new standards. And so he took advantage of a world in flux, just as a wise investor snaps up bargains and helps stabilize economic chaos at the low ebb of a bearish stock market. After all, it was not so much the good-will of governmental authorities, expressed or tacit, as it was the naïve and pliable mood of a new theatregoing public that enabled him to attain his goal.

[230]

In the long view, of course, the most momentous relations a statesman, a writer or a theatre has the privilege of fulfilling are those with an international public. As experience has proved, during the war and since, it is the artist in general and the artist of the theatre in particular who makes the best diplomat. The professional diplomat and the propagandist are inept and clumsy agents in comparison, for their methods, unlike those of the actor and the musician, do not reach across frontiers to the heart and soul and emotions of the populace of a sister nation. In this sense, therefore, the Moscow Art Theatre through its several branches is the ambassador extraordinary and minister plenipotentiary from the Russian people to the American people.

Why, then, is the Soviet Government so meticulous about granting leave of absence from Russia and permission for these and other artists to come to America? Why does it set limits to the absence of Chaliapin? Why does it forbid the simultaneous departure of both Stanislavsky and Nemirovitch-Dantchenko? For an answer that explains this seemingly paradoxical policy, we must turn to the realm of economics. When the balance of trade or some other factor in international finance begins to draw too heavily on a country's gold reserves, that country immediately establishes an embargo on the exportation of the precious metal. In the case of contemporary Russia, for the first time in modern history so far as I know, a comparable situation has arisen in the realm of art. Attracted by material prizes and by the same curiosity regarding the outside world which that world at large has suddenly conceived in regard to Russia, the artists of Moscow and Leningrad, to a man, are consumed with the passion for travel. Left to its own course, the exodus would show such an unfavorable balance of esthetic trade that the theatres and concert halls would have to close their doors. Russia's golden hoard of art belongs to the world, and there is no Russian who is not proud of the fact that the world values and appreciates it at its true worth. But Russia's rulers are within their rights in insisting that her esthetic balance must not be permitted to dwindle and disappear.

INDEX

Index